THE Bovington

TANK COLLECTION

Including Other Armoured Fighting Vehicles

George and Adam Forty

Ensign

First Published 1992

Ensign Publications,
a division of Hampshire Books Ltd.,
2 Redcar Street,
Southampton SO1 5LL
United Kingdom

Tel. 01929405096

ISBN 185455 055 1

British Library Cataloguing in Publication Data
Forty, George
The Bovington tank collection including other armoured fighting vehicles.
1. Armoured combat vehicles, history
I. Title II. Forty, Adam
623.747509

Publisher: David Graves
Editor: Michael G. Burns
Typesetting: PageMerger
Printed by Graficas London Ltd.

Contents

World War Two

Post War Years

Introduction

Origins of the Collection

The collection of armoured fighting vehicles (AFVs) at the Tank Museum, Bovington Camp, is one of the largest and most comprehensive collections in the world, containing over two hundred and sixty major exhibits from twenty three different countries, as far afield as Australia, Brazil, Japan and Russia. The collection has been built up steadily over the past sixty-five years, starting after the Great War, when large numbers of World War One British tanks were brought to Bovington to be broken up and sold for scrap. Twenty-six specimens, examples of each Mark of current or experimental vehicle, were collected and moved into a small fenced compound on the heath to the north of the Camp. This was the beginning of the present museum.

In 1923, Rudyard Kipling during a visit to Bovington expressed disappointment that so little was being done to preserve these unique machines. The following year, a start was made by housing a selection of them – including *Little Willie*, the first experimental tank ever built, and *Big Willie*, or *Mother* as it was more popularly called within the Tank Corps, the first gun tank – in an open-sided shed at the Driving and Maintenance Wing of what was then the Royal Tank Corps Central Schools.

During the inter-war years, the collection was enlarged by the addition of various experimental machines. However, when war was declared, the collection suffered from the drive for scrap steel which destroyed many irreplaceable relics, among them *Mother,* the experimental electric-driven tank, General Martel's own home-made tank, the Medium 'C' and many other unique machines. Fortunately, others were saved, by being used during the invasion scare of 1940 – the Vickers Medium and the *Independent*, for example covered the road from Bovington to Wool, while other Museum tanks guarded the coast near Lulworth Cove.

In 1945, space for some fifty vehicles was again found at the D & M School, but the buildings were not very suitable, so between 1947 and 1952, the present central hangar was taken into use. A fine collection of Allied and foreign AFVs which had been accumulated during World War Two for investigation and experimental purposes was added in 1951. The collection remained fairly stable for the next thirty years, growing slowly until, by 1981, it numbered about one hundred and twenty AFVs in all.

The next major expansion of the collection came in 1981, with the arrival of the present curator and was part of his overall plan to modernise and improve the Tank Museum. AFVs have been obtained, mainly through exchanges with other museums or as gifts, from all over the world. Much work has also been done on the restoration of AFVs within the collection and, for the very first time, a small conservation workshop was established in 1984. Many AFVs have been restored and in 1989, the workshop staff won a Scania/Transport Award for its restoration work. In the winter 1990/1991, a small purpose-built workshop was erected, so the museum restoration staff now have a permanent home.

The contribution made by the Society of Friends of the Tank Museum deserves special mention. They have played a major role in obtaining and restoring AFVs for the collection. This has involved, for example, a visit to assist the Finns, leading to the donation of the T26 and a second Stug, while Bob Grundy and his Tracked Armour Group, are currently completing full restoration of a Matilda I and a Churchill AVRE.

Following the highly successful armoured operations of the Gulf War in early 1991, the collection was further increased by a selection of captured Iraqi AFVs, mainly of Soviet origin. These have been on show in the Post War Hull since July 1991, however, it is hoped to build a separate Gulf War Hull in due course.

Purposes of the Museum

The collection has four main purposes: education, research and development, recruiting and entertainment.

EDUCATION The history of the development of the armoured fighting vehicle and of armoured warfare can be studied in detail by both military and civilian researchers.

RESEARCH & DEVELOPMENT Full use is made of the Museum's collection and archives by both military and defence industry personnel, so that those concerned with future development can learn from the past.

RECRUITING Being the Corps Museum of the Royal Armoured Corps and the Regimental Museum of the Royal Tank Regiment means that the Tank Museum is an ideal location to show the history and traditions of these Regiments.

ENTERTAINMENT The Tank Museum first opened its doors to the general public in 1947, when some two thousand five hundred visitors attended without charge. Now the average paid attendance is one hundred and seventy-five to two hundred thousand annually, and the proceeds from the admission charges, shops, restaurant, etc, have enabled an adequate-sized staff to be employed and the collection to be better looked after and maintained than ever before.

Curatorial policy
The present curatorial policy is to divide the collection under four main headings:

   a.   AFVs for static display in the exhibition halls.
   b.   AFVs for mobile use, such as at Battle Day and other events (including film and television work).
   c.   Reserve AFVs, awaiting restoration, or for exchange purposes.
   d.   AFVs on temporary or permanent loan at selected locations.

Static displays account for the largest part of the collection. Some of these AFVs are in diorama settings, some repainted and 'badged' to various units of the Royal Armoured Corps, while others have been left in their original, authentic paint schemes. The internal displays are altered from time to time and since the expansion programme began in 1983, new EVOLUTION, WORLD WAR ONE, INTER WAR, POST WAR, EXPERIMENTAL VEHICLES & CARRIERS Halls have all been built, some £2 million having been raised over the past 10 years to fund this expansion. 1993 will see the completion of new diorama displays in the WORLD WAR TWO Hall, thus ending that phase of the expansion. A separate small Costume Collection has been added in a World War Two 'spider' hut on the far side of the carpark, which now also contains woodworking and display workshops, plus uniform and artifact storage. A special 'Lawrence of Arabia' exhibition is also planned there for 1992. All this work is carried out by the Museum's own staff and we are always grateful for donations of suitable artifacts or finance with which to improve our displays.

The fleet of running AFVs grows every year, the aim being to have a representative selection of AFVs through the ages, in particular from Great Britain, so that they can take part in mobility displays, parades, pageants, and so on. Taking into consideration the difficulties of obtaining spare parts, provision of fuel, movement to and from locations, insurance and crewing, etc, the Museum's AFVs have still succeeded in playing an increasingly active part in public events, helped on many occasions by the Friends of the Tank Museum. This has recently included the 1991 Royal Tournament, when six museum AFVs took part, driven by museum staff and commanded by Friends. Some static and mobile film and television work is also undertaken, with the primary object of raising funds for the Museum. It must never be forgotten that the Tank Museum is a Registered Charity and receives no regular funds from the Ministry of Defence or any other source, so must raise its own finances. All monies raised from any source are used for the good of the collection.

Recent AFV exchanges have included deals with France, West Germany, New Zealand, Finland and the Soviet Union. The Tank Museum endeavours to maintain a small number of spare AFVs for exchange purposes, but is always delighted to accept donations of suitable AFVs. In certain cases, Friends of the Tank Museum have put their own AFVs on loan, for exhibition or mobility purposes.

A small number of AFVs are on permanent loan, the most notable one being the Heavy Mark IV Female *Flirt II*, which is presently on display at the Museum of Lincolnshire Life, in recognition of the fact that Lincoln was the location of William Foster & Co Ltd, where both *Little Willie* and *Mother* were built. From time to time AFVs go on temporary loan, to Regiments of the Royal Armoured Corps for special events, and sometimes to other museums.

Archives

Although this book is primarily about the AFVs in the collection, mention must be made of the vast numbers of handbooks, workshop manuals, engineering drawings, parts lists, military manuals, papers, books and photographs, which are held in the Library and Photographic Library, available for study. They are constantly in use by authors, modellers and war-gamers from all over the world, their queries being handled by the Librarian and his staff. Queries can in some cases be answered by post, while the Library Reading Room is open to callers (preferably by appointment), during weekdays.

Contents of this book

This book is, we hope, the first of a new series which will cover all the important AFVs in the Tank Museum's unique collection. In it we have deliberately tried to cover all periods of the remarkable development of the AFV and not merely to pick out the 'gems' of the collection, but rather to give an 'across the board' picture of the depth and variety which exists here. Where possible we have included information about the actual Museum exhibit, but sadly in some cases this information is non-existent, at least within current Museum records. We are always interested in hearing from anyone with information about a particular AFV, especially those on which we have little detailed information.

This book is not meant to take the place of the Museum guide, but rather to supplement it, by providing the interested visitor with just a little more information, which we hope will be of value to all who come to the Tank Museum or have an interest in the fascinating history of the armoured fighting vehicle.

Please note that all photographs in this book are copyright to the Tank Museum and must not be reproduced without permission. Many of them have been taken by our resident photographer, Roland Groom, to whom we extend our sincere thanks for his invaluable help. We must also thank David Fletcher, the Museum Librarian, for his assistance and support.

ADAM & GEORGE FORTY
Bryantspuddle
September 1991

The Hornsby, possibly the oldest working track-layer in the world, being driven by Museum Librarian David Fletcher.

Hornsby Chain Track Tractor
SERIAL NO 35082

The 1909 Hornsby Chain Track Tractor was the last of a series of primitive tracklayers whose origins lay in a directive from the British War Office of 1903, for the organization of a tractor trial. A prize of £1,000 would be awarded for a military tractor which could run over a 40-mile course, carrying its own fuel and a 16-ton load.

At this trial the only serious contender was a wheeled engine designed by Richard Hornsby & Son of Grantham, Lincolnshire. The £1,000 prize went to the Hornsby which easily met and surpassed the authorities' requirements to the extent of being awarded a bonus of £180. Following these successful trials, David Roberts, who had joined Hornsby's in 1895 as Chief Engineer and had become Managing Director in 1904, conceived, developed and patented a chain track system. He sold the idea to the War Office's Mechanical Transport Committee and, as a result, the prize-winning tractor of the 1903 trials was converted from wheels to tracks in August 1906. This modified machine then took part in further trials at Aldershot in 1907. In 1909, the Army finally ordered three wheeled Hornsby Tractors, with 50 hp, four-cylinder, oil-fuelled engines, and one 60 hp Caterpillar (Ser No: 35082). Soon afterwards, a further three wheeled tractors were purchased. Thus, apart from the machine modified in 1906, ours is the only Hornsby/Roberts to see military service.

Caterpillar 35082 was delivered to Aldershot in 1910, having driven all the way from Grantham! In 1911, it was converted to petrol with a substantial increase in power, to 105 hp. However, lack of customer interest caused Hornsby's to sell the rights of the track-layer design, for £4,000, to the American Holt Manufacturing Company, which later became the Caterpillar Tractor Company.

Much of the design of the vehicle is reminiscent of its cousin and contemporary, the steam traction engine. The make of the engine is uncertain although the six cylinders cast in pairs, and other parts, are marked with raised serial numbers prefixed by the letters PPV. It was probably the maker's own product.

The tracks, one of the first types produced in Britain, and the brainchild of David Roberts, are of the rigid girder type. They flex only in an inward direction, locking out to form a fixed trackway under pressure. They are formed by a complex series of castings with replaceable wooden inserts to absorb wear.

Sitting in the driver's seat covered only by an overhanging canopy one is confronted by, as one driver put it, a 'puzzling array of levers and wheels with many little brass plates telling you what they are for.' One of the most advanced design

A Hornsby tractor being used as an artillery gun limber.

features lies in the steering which is controlled by a large wheel on a vertical stem which acts upon the output shafts of the differential by means of band brakes. Also on the upright shaft of the steering column is a hand throttle lever and underneath, on the floor, two pedals for clutch and brake. There are also levers for the four-speed gear change (with a separate one for engaging reverse), and a differential lock and levers to lock or declutch the drive sprockets on each side.

Before WWI, a Capt T.G. Tulloch did suggest fitting 35082 with an armoured superstructure, thus anticipating the idea of the tank. However, this was never done and the Hornsby tractor played no direct part in the evolution of 'Little Willie'.

In 1910, the Hornsby performed well at a Royal Artillery practice camp at Traws-fynydd in North Wales, where it was used to haul heavy guns. It reportedly upset the horses and this was the last active service it saw. Throughout the Great War it remained in store at Avonmouth, where Sir John Carden's ASC Company was based. This Company was responsible for unloading Holt Caterpillars from USA and preparing them for service on the Western Front.

35082 was driven out during the Victory Celebrations, it also took part in at least one Royal Tournament and a small number of RASC historical pageants between the wars. It was then placed in the RASC Museum, (now the Royal Corps of Transport Museum) Aldershot. It was restored to full running order by 18 Command Workshop REME, Bovington Camp in 1958. Finally, in 1958, the RASC Museum generously donated it to the Tank Museum where it has pride of place in the Evolution Hall.

It was last driven on 9th October 1984 by David Fletcher, the Tank Museum Librarian, who commented: 'It was a great surprise to discover just how easy the driving was and it makes one wonder why this system was not adapted to suit the first tanks instead of the unwieldy method actually employed.'

SPECIFICATIONS

Manufacturer:	Richard Hornsby & Son, Lincolnshire
Pattern Date:	1909
Condition:	runner (November 1984)
Engine:	105 hp, 6-cylinder, petrol-fuelled
Armour:	nil
Armament:	nil
Max. Speed:	7.5 mph (12 kmph)
Range:	100 miles
Crew:	1 or 2
Length:	15'10"
Height:	9'8"
Width:	5'9"
Weight:	8.5 tons

Little Willie

At the beginning of World War One, the War Office was only interested in mechanization for transportation and supply. It was left to the efforts of more unconventional minds to initiate the process and idea of the tank. The more noted of these were Colonel Ernest Swinton, the British Army's official war correspondent in France, and Winston Churchill, then First Lord of the Admiralty. With the war in stalemate after the First Battle of Ypres in 1914, trench warfare ensued, halting further advance by either the Germans or the Allies. The problem was that with machine-guns, artillery shells and miles of barbed-wire barricades, the formidable lines of opposing trenches which stretched from Nieuport on the Belgian coast to Switzerland, had brought the fighting to a grinding halt. The idea evolved to produce a machine in which to cross no-man's land safe from the hail of German machine gun bullets. Swinton took this a step further as he explained in his book *Eyewitness*:

> Throughout this time I had been wracking my brains to discover an antidote; and within the last two weeks my vague idea of an armoured vehicle had definitely crystallised in the form of a power-driven, bullet-proof, armed engine, capable of destroying machine-guns, of crossing country and trenches, of breaking through entanglements, and of climbing earthworks.

The haphazard way in which the idea of the armoured vehicle was being developed all changed on 22nd February 1915. This was the date of the first meeting of an Admiralty team set up by Winston Churchill, then First Lord of the Admiralty, called the Landships Committee. The basis of their work on the Swinton proposals was encapsulated in a memorandum he submitted to the General Staff in France, entitled 'The Necessity for Machine-Gun Destroyers', in which he proposed the following more detailed specifications for the new weapons:

> These machines would be petrol tractors on the caterpillar principle, of a type which can travel at 4 miles an hour on the flat, can cross a ditch up to 4 ft width without climbing, can climb in and out of a broader cavity and can scramble over a breastwork. It is possible to build such tractors. They should be armoured with hardened steel plate, proof against the German steel cored, armour-piercing and reversed bullets and armed with – say – two Maxims and a Maxim 2-pdr gun.

The Number 1 Lincoln Machine, with Bullock tracks and, underneath the tarpaulin, a dummy turret.

Little Willie on trial at Burton Park in December 1915. Notice the new tracks, invented by William Tritton, with their armoured frames.

The Committee, under the Chairmanship of Sir Eustace Tennyson d'Eyncourt, Director of Naval Construction, appointed as technical adviser to the project Colonel Rookes Evelyn Bell Crompton, who had already been enthusiastically sending various of his ideas to the War Office. On his appointment Crompton was seventy years old but, as an old soldier and a highly skilled engineer, he took his work seriously and imported a variety of commercial tractors from the United States for evaluation. At this time the United States had become large scale manufacturers and vendors of tracklayers in the world market, due to the scale and variety of their agricultural industry. Crompton also came up with various ideas for articulated landcrawlers on the drawing board and had ordered a set of Bullock Creeping Grip tracks, again from the USA. Ironically, as mentioned previously, it had been Hornsbys, who in 1912, had sold the rights of their track-layer design to the American Holt Manufacturing Company, which later became known as the Caterpillar Tractor Co., for £4,000 (*see* Hornsby Chain Track Tractor). Unfortunately, Crompton's desire for perfection conflicted with the exigencies of war.

With Crompton prevaricating, the Committee grew impatient and so a brilliant young draughtsman from William Foster's works at the Wellington Foundry, Lincoln, was called in to help with the drawings. Mr Rigby, who was then Foster's Chief Draughtsman, arrived in Kensington in July 1915 but was given little to do except some sketches, and so was called back to Lincoln within the month.

In late July, the Landships Committee finally lost patience with the elderly Crompton so Albert Stern, Secretary to the Committee, offered the entire project to William Foster's. On 1st August, William Tritton, Managing Director of Fosters, on receiving the Contract for the work immediately cabled from London: 'take a Daimler set and build it into a box such as Rigby drew. Use tracks that are on their way over.' The Daimler set which Tritton mentioned was the engine, gearbox and differential from a Foster-Daimler artillery tractor. Eventually, the main chassis frame and radiator were also used.

The similarity between the 'box' mentioned in Tritton's cable and the box part of Crompton's Mark 3 articulated design seem more than coincidental and Crompton himself was of the opinion that his ideas had been used. After the war, in 1919, both sides gave their evidence before a Royal Commission on Awards to Inventors. Both Tritton and Rigby were questioned and both denied that any of Crompton's ideas had been used. Sadly, Crompton never received the rewards he richly deserved for his research, which had, at the very least, pointed Tritton and Foster's in the right direction.

On 5th August, the two pairs of lengthened Bullock Creeping Grip Tractor tracks which had been ordered from Chicago by Crompton, arrived at the docks in Liverpool and were forwarded to Lincoln. In just over a month, on 10th September, the vehicle was running. On 19th September 1915 the 'Number 1 Lincoln Machine' as it was then designated was tested at Cross-o-Cliffe Field, Lincoln, with disastrous results as it kept shedding its tracks!

The basic problem was that the tracks were designed for commercial not military use. They could not adequately support the weight of the hull and fell off whenever the machine tried to climb over a trench. Tritton was aided by Lt Walter Gordon Wilson RNVR a pioneer designer and 'engineer of undoubted genius' (designer of the 1902 Wilson Pilcher Motor Car), who had joined him in April 1915, acting as overseer for the Landships Committee. They realized that no other commercial tracks would meet their needs, so began the task of designing their own. Eventually, they settled on an idea of Tritton's for a 'crude but durable form of track composed of flat plates of cast steel, with a lip at the after end, riveted to cast inner links that were hinged together.' Each plate was about 20 inches (50 cm) wide.

On reflection, it is clear that this was the main feature that made the British tank so successful, as, apart from the French Renault, all other vehicles used the basic Holt tractor suspension and track. This obviously meant that the vehicle design was limited to the commercial specifications inherent in the Holt's system.

At last using Tritton's track system and the rebuilt Lincoln Machine, without its dummy turret which raised the vehicle's centre of gravity too high, *Little Willie*, was born. The name was a derogatory reference to the Kaiser. At the rear, a hydraulic jack controlled the movement of the tail assembly. This was used both to assist with steering and to alter the balance of the vehicle when crossing trenches or ascending steep banks, although if it was being steered by its tracks, the wheels could be lifted clear of the ground. On 3rd December 1915, *Little Willie* now weighing in at around 14 tons was ready for trials.

The trials were a great success for, although the overall performance figures had not improved, the tracks remained firmly in place throughout. It could manage a 2-foot vertical step, cross a 4-foot trench and move cross country at a steady 2 mph, reduced to mph over obstacles and trenches. From this time on, *Little Willie* was exclusively used for training purposes, as the braked differential method of steering was also used in later Marks of fighting tanks. It is therefore not surprising, that at the 1919 Royal Commission on Awards to Inventors, the contribution of Wilson and Tritton was adjudged to be 'worthy of the highest award.'

On 29th January and 8th February 1916, further trials were held in Hatfield Park, Herts. *Little Willie*'s rival was *Mother*, which was shown to be better, exceeding all expectations of those watching except Colonel Crompton who renamed *Mother* 'The Slug'! In 1916, *Little Willie* was once more re-appraised, during design work on the lighter medium tank (the Whippet) and at around this time the wheeled steering tail was removed. Most of the insides were removed after the war and the front plate damaged even later. Between the wars it also arrived in Bovington and became part of the newly conceived tank collection of the Tank Corps kept outside on waste-ground in Bovington Camp. and later in an open-sided shed. Stories that it was used to protect an airfield during WW2 are probably false (see section on the Peerless armoured car), so it was fortunate to escape the clutches of the scrap drive which destroyed so many other treasured relics.

It has remained part of the collection ever since and is now housed in the Evolution Hall in a diorama setting depicting William Foster's factory in Lincoln. Arrangements are in hand to build a full size mock-up engine and transmission to replace those items which have been removed.

SPECIFICATIONS

Manufacturer:	William Foster & Co. Ltd, Lincoln.
Pattern Date:	1915
Condition:	non-runner
Engine:	Daimler, 6-cylinder, sleeve-valve, petrol-fuelled, 105 bhp at 1000 rpm
Armament:	nil
Armour:	boiler-plate
Crew:	5 (2 drivers, 3 crew)
Max. Speed:	3.5 mph (5.63 kmph)
Range:	unknown
Length:	5.87 m
Height:	2.51 m
Width:	2.86 m
Weight:	14.22 tons

Mark I Male
702

On 8th May 1919, a presentation of a Mark I tank was made to James, 4th Marquess of Salisbury KG, to commemorate the secret tank trials and inspection held in his grounds at Hatfield Park between January 26th and February 8th 1916, which was witnessed by various dignitaries including His Majesty King George V.

On 2nd January 1916, Albert Stern, a member of the influential Landships Committee, had at last found a site suitable for holding the secret trials of the prototype landships *Little Willie* and HMLS *Centipede* (the latter was also known as *Mother* and *Big Willie*), both designed and built by William Foster and Co. Ltd, of Lincoln. The site for the mock battlefield and swamp he had selected was Hatfield Park. On 26th January, the first vehicle, HMLS *Centipede* arrived, now renamed a 'tank' for security reasons. The name was invented by Lt Colonel W. Dally-Jones and by Colonel Ernest Swinton, who explained in a letter to The Marquess of Salisbury KG, GCVO, CB:

> The origin of this word is as follows: At a conference on the 24th December, 1915, it was pointed out that the then official term of 'landships' was a sheer give-away of the whole thing. Lieut. Colonel W. Dally Jones, Assistant Secretary of the War Cabinet, and I in consultation together within the next two or three days evolved the word – 'Tank'. It was consequently incorporated in the report of the Conference of the 24th December 1916.

He also states later in this letter:

> it may interest you to know that the words *Big and Little Willie* were applied by me to HMLS *Centipede* (Mark I Tank) and it's predecessor, when nestling alongside each other in the mud, on the golf course, in your park in January 1916.

The 29th January saw a preliminary, unofficial inspection of HMLS *Centipede*'s performance across the battlefield and on 2nd February an official inspection by the authorities including the First Lord of the Admiralty, the Secretary of State for War and the Minister of Munitions. Swinton also attended and later recalled:

> Wednesday, 2 February, was the great day of the official trial. So far as was humanly possible everything had been done to ensure that there should be no breakdown. On this point I was particularly nervous, for so much hung in the balance… it is the first impression that counts… The demonstration was attended by Lord Kitchener, Mr Balfour, Mr Lloyd George, Mr McKenna, members of the Admiralty Staff, General Robertson, several senior officers from the War Office, those connected with the creation of *Mother*, and last but not least, representatives of GHQ.

The trial was a great success, *Mother* had proven her ability easily to meet the requirements set by the War Office. These were that the vehicle should be capable of lifting itself over a 4-foot 6-inch (1.37-m) parapet and cross an 8-foot (2.5-m) wide trench. D'Eyncourt, then a Lt. Colonel in command of the 6th Royal Scots Fusiliers, later wrote to Churchill:

> The official tests of trenches, etc., were nothing to it, and finally we showed them how it could cross a nine foot gap after climbing a four foot six inch high perpendicular parapet. Wire entanglements it goes through like a rhinoceros through a field of corn.

Of the observers only a few were left unmoved, Lord Kitchener thought the new tank was merely a 'pretty mechanical toy', while Colonel Crompton renamed *Mother* 'The Slug'. However, the opinions of the representatives of GHQ had the most weight. They agreed to recommend to the Commander-in-Chief that he ask for some machines. His Majesty the King, who was keeping abreast of the situation, now said he would like to see HMLS *Centipede*, so on 8th February a private trial was held. The King, who followed every manoeuvre with great attention, expressed his satisfaction and even congratulated the driver personally.

Mother crossing a ditch during the Burton Park trials in 1916. The tail wheels, seen at the rear of the tank, were intended to improve the obstacle crossing ability of the tank and also provide aid in steering the heavy vehicle. The Mark I was the only heavy tank to have these tail wheels, which were dropped in the later models, as they were ineffective.

The response from the War Office was to order a mere forty machines, Swinton reacted quickly:

Considering the nature of the weapon and the way in which it was to be employed, this number was, to my mind, quite inadequate and I suggested that it should be increased to at least 100. This was the number finally decided upon.

Before long, the order was increased to 150. The Metropolitan Carriage, Wagon and Finance Company Ltd of Oldbury, Birmingham, was awarded the bulk of the contract, while Foster's would build just twenty-five. Initially, the Mark 1 heavy tanks resulting from this order were, apart from a few minor improvements, essentially the same as *Mother*, except in having armour. *Mother* had been completed in unarmoured boiler plate, service machines were built of armoured plate (at its thickest 10 mm on the Mark 1) capable of resisting enemy machine-gun fire. However, after further consideration, some people realised that, armed with six-pounders, tanks would be adequately equipped for attacking machine-gun posts and strong points, but would be almost useless against a determined attack by massed infantry. It was decided, therefore, to arm only half the order with six-pounders while the other half would be built with different sponsons to carry Vickers machine-guns. These were given their biological classification by Swinton who named the Mark 1 armed with six-pounders 'Male' and those with machine-guns 'Female'.

The Mark 1 Tank first saw action late in 1916.The great Somme offensive had begun on 1st July and on the very first day the British alone suffered sixty thousand casualties, one-third killed. It was the heaviest loss the British Army had ever known and all in vain as the German defences were impenetrable. All available vehicles were moved up from their improvised training area at Yvrench, near Abbeville, arriving at Bray-sur-Somme, close behind the front on the 13th, where they were loaded up and prepared for action. General Sir Douglas Haig, Commander-in-Chief British Expeditionary Force decide to spread all the available tanks, forty-nine in total, in twos and threes across the entire front. Zero hour would be 0620 hours on the 15th.

On the morning of 15th September 1915 at 05.15 hours, engines were started and vehicles began to leave for their start point. The very first tank in action, D1 (which should have been accompanied by two others, which unfortunately broke down), commanded by Captain H. W. Mortimer supported by two companies of the 6th Kings Own Yorkshire Light Infantry, advanced across no-man's land. Immune to enemy bullets and with guns blazing, D1 advanced on the German lines. The shattering psychological effect on the Germans can only be imagined, but by the time D1 reached the German trenches they were deserted by all but the dead. On

15

arriving there, D1 waited for the infantry to come up and at this moment the steering gear was struck by a shell (possibly German but just as possibly from the British barrage) and was put out of action.

Another of the tanks in the action that morning was C 19 *Clan Leslie*, Capt A. Holcroft Walker's tank, who commanded 4 Section of C Coy. It was painted in a multi-coloured disruptive camouflage pattern devised by Col Solomon J. Solomon,

C19 'Clan Leslie' in Chimpanzee Valley on the Somme. The screen, made of wood and chicken wire, covering the top of the tank is to protect against grenades.

RA and fitted with a wire netting roof (to deflect hand grenades). It broke down going into action with tail assembly trouble, but had been photographed in Chimpanzee Valley before the battle, so formed the ideal model for our Mark I's paint scheme.

Of the forty-nine tanks due to fight, only thirty-two reached the start point for the attack. Of these, only a handful returned intact. However, Haig was delighted. Everywhere that the attack had been supported by tanks, it had succeeded; wherever the attack had not been supported by tanks, it had failed.

After the War on 2nd April 1919 Churchill wrote the Marquess of Salisbury the following letter:

War Office
Whitehall

2nd April 1919

My Dear Salisbury,

It would give the Army Council and myself very real pleasure if you would consent to accept one of the original Tanks to put in your Park at Hatfield.

I need not say again what my predecessors and I have felt as to the immense help you gave the Government when the tanks were at first a matter of experiment, by allowing us to make trials in secret at Hatfield, and I thought you would perhaps like to have one of the earliest types as a memento of the days when we were allowed to make free with the privacy of your grounds.

Yours
Winston Churchill

The Museum's Mark I was delivered at Hatfield on 7th or 8th of May 1919. Finally, after fifty years at Hatfield Park, the Mark 1 was presented by Robert 5th Marquess of Salisbury KG PC to the Royal Armoured Corps Tank Museum and was moved there on 7th May 1969.

SPECIFICATIONS:

Manufacturer:	William Foster & Co, Lincoln.
Pattern Date:	1915
Condition:	non-runner
Engine:	Daimler, 6-cylinder, in-line, double sleeve-valve, petrol-fuelled, water-cooled 105 bhp at 1000 rpm
Max. Speed:	3.7 mph
Range:	23 miles
Armour:	6-12mm
Armament:	2 6 pdr (57mm) guns of 40 calibre. 4 .303-inch Hotchkiss machine-guns
Crew:	8 (Commander, driver, 2 secondary gearsmen/gunners, 4 gunners)
Length:	26'5" (32'6" with tail)
Height:	8'1½"
Width:	13'9"
Weight:	28 tons

Mark IV Male
NO 2324

Haig was so delighted with the tanks' success at Flers that he ordered 1,000 more to be built. These appeared in 1917 as the Mark IV (Mk II & III having been produced in minimal quantities only) and later a further 200 were ordered. A total of 1,015 were actually built of which 420 were male and 595 were female. Again the Mk IV was only altered in the following relatively minor details over the Mk I.

The petrol tanks were placed on the outside of the vehicle at the rear, protected by the track frames, considerably minimising the danger to the crew when the tank was hit. The petrol was fed to the carburettor by the Autovac system, replacing the gravity feed system used on the Mark 1. The armour was increased over vital portions from 10mm to 12mm. The 6 pdr guns were reduced in length to 23 calibre, and Lewis guns replaced the Hotchkiss machine-guns. The sponsons were reduced in size, and were so made that they could be pushed into the hull when travelling by rail. (They were laboriously unbolted and removed for rail travel on the Mark 1). A silencer and an exhaust pipe to disperse the fumes to the rear were introduced. Track rollers and sprockets were strengthened. Coventry chains were increased in strength and chain guards provided to keep them clear of mud. External communications were arranged with the Infantry by means of discs, and internal communication from the driver to the gearsman was arranged by coloured lights. Anti-splash devices were provided. Armoured unditching beams, about ten feet long and a foot square and provided with a heavy chain were supported on rails which ran along the top of the hull. (This was used when the vehicle was bogged down in mud. The beam was chained to the tracks and hauled round with them. Once the beam wedged itself beneath the vehicle the tracks had something to bite on and could lever itself out of trouble). Steel spuds were introduced to increase the bearing surface on the track.

The tank in the museum is No 2324 (Training No 102), and was built by the Metropolitan Carriage, Wagon and Finance Company of Birmingham in 1917.

In April, of the previous year, the Royal Navy had come forward to offer help in gunnery training for men of the Army's new Heavy Branch Machine-Gun Corps,

A Mark IV Male climbing a test ramp at Erin, September 1917.

A column of heavy tanks moving through London, probably on a War Bond drive.

which later became the Tank Corps and eventually the Royal Tank Regiment. The Army had been hard pressed to provide trained crews in the summer of 1916, for the first six tank companies. By the time of the Battle of Cambrai in November 1917, the Tank Corps had expanded to nine battalions! On 1st May 1919, in recognition of the Royal Navy's help in training 136 officers and 2,412 gun-layers between April 1916 and late 1917, tank No 2324 (used on Tank Corps training duties at Bovington, Wareham and Lulworth between 1917 and 1919) was presented to HMS *Excellent*, the Royal Navy's Gunnery Training establishment at Whale Island, Portsmouth, by Brigadier-General E. B. Matthew Lannowe.

For twenty years No 2324 remained part of the Royal Navy's static equipment at HMS *Excellent*. In 1939, with the outbreak of World War Two, the tank was restored to full serviceability, under the direction of Captain A. Menhinick, Royal Artillery (later RNVR) who was temporarily attached with a battery of four guns to Whale Island. Spare parts for the restoration were used, with permission of Portsmouth Corporation, from a Mark 1V which had stood as a war memorial on Southsea Common. In addition to the tank's normal ground fighting armament which comprised two 6 pdr guns, two .303 Hotchkiss and two .303 Lewis machine-guns, No 2324 was fitted with a Lewis gun for anti-aircraft use. The tank was crewed by the Royal Navy, flew the White Ensign and carried the name *Excellent* and the initials 'RN' at bow and stern. *Excellent* then became operational with the RN battalion allocated for the defence of Portsmouth – but damaged a private car on its first outing and was not allowed out of barracks again!

From after the war until 1971, *Excellent* remained immobile at Whale Island, but in 1969 restoration work again started to reverse the ravaging effect of fifty years of life spent out in the open at the mercy of the wind and rain. However, in 1971 a decision was made to hand back this historic machine to the Army for preservation at the Royal Armoured Corps Tank Museum, Bovington Camp. Three years of careful, devoted work followed at 18 Command Workshop REME, itself a direct descendant of the original Tank Corps Workshop established in Bovington in 1917 and still occupying the same buildings! Using original drawings and specifications, and with the valuable co-operation and assistance of Wellworthy Ltd of Lymington, the Workshop restored *Excellent* once more to full running order.

Since this time, *Excellent* has only left the Museum on two occasions, both in the summer of 1984. It first caused a stir at the British Army Equipment Exhibition. David Fletcher, Museum Librarian, commented:

> Every time we left our stand and strolled down to see how it was getting on we found a small queue composed of the top brass of every nation you can think of patiently waiting their turn for a peer through the open sponson door.

Shortly following *Excellent*'s return to the museum, work began preparing it for use in the highly acclaimed television series *Soldiers*. A crew comprising men of the 1st Royal Tank Regiment together with Lt Colonel Ken Hill, the Museum Assistant Curator, and David Fletcher, manned the tank, dressed in period uniforms. The tank was driven over the Museum picnic area which had been adapted to represent a World War One battlefield – complete with spectacular explosions, provided by the

The Museum's tank HMS Excellent leaving Whale Island in 1940. It was taken to Portsmouth where it served for town defence patrols.

Beutepanzerwagen IV; Mark IV Male captured at Cambrai, rearmed with a Russian Sokol 57mm gun.

BBC Special Effects Department. The tank was seen driving through a smokescreen firing its guns with the aid of charges placed in the barrels of the 6 pounders and firing blanks from it's machine-guns. David Fletcher who was driving, recalled:

> Once the clutch was let in there was nothing more to do but watch the producer and signal for the guns; the tank rolled along on a dead straight course with Colonel Hill blazing away with the Lewis in the cab and two Hotchkiss firing from the sides. Some of the explosions shook the tank, while the crash of the six-pounder added to the illusion of action.

SPECIFICATIONS

Manufacturer:	Metropolitan Carriage Works and William Foster
Pattern Date:	1917
Condition:	runner (1984)
Engine:	Daimler, 6-cylinder, in-line, double sleeve-valve, 105 bhp at 1000 rpm
Max. Speed:	3.7 mph
Range:	35 miles
Armour:	6 - 12 mm
Armament:	2 6 pounders (57mm) 23 calibre Hotchkiss QF guns. 2 .303-inch Hotchkiss machine-guns and 2 .303-inch Lewis Guns (plus one x AA Lewis when tank was at Whale Island only) mounted for anti-aircraft use.
Crew:	8 (Commander, driver, 2 secondary gearsmen/gunners, 4 gunners)
Length:	26'5"
Height:	8'2"
Width:	13'6"
Weight:	28 tons

Mark V Male
TANK NO 9199

The first 'one man drive' tank to be produced of the heavy tanks, the Mark V was designed in August 1917, was running by January 1918 and in the hands of troops by May 1918. It was first used in action in France at Hamel, in July 1918. In all 400 were built (50% Male and 50% Female) between December 1917 and June 1918. It incorporated various improvements made to the Mark IV. The engine, a 150 bhp six-cylinder petrol-fuelled Ricardo, was designed with the requirement that it should run for one hundred hours without adjustment to the bearings, etc, and that it should be able to run on 'inferior petrol'. The internal communications were improved by using voice pipes and externally a semaphore was introduced to signal from tank to tank or to other troops, but its design was not very satisfactory, being too heavy and liable to jam due to bullet splash. This was the first tank that could be driven by the driver alone. This was accomplished by the fitting of epicyclic gearing designed by Major W. G. Wilson. This enabled the driver to alter the speed of either track independently. Frontal armour was increased to 14mm. Splash plates were fitted and observation was improved by means of extra ports, better periscopes and rotary peephole covers. Introduction of a raised cab at the rear, similar in size to the driver's cab, it provided better all round vision and a secure place from which to attach the unditching beam (see Mark IV for further details). Escape hatches at the rear were introduced as well as an extra mounting point for a machine-gun to cover a blind spot in which the enemy could gather behind the vehicle. Ventilation inside the vehicle was also improved.

Tank No 9199 was issued to the 8th Battalion, Tank Corps in July 1918. They were the first Battalion to receive the Mark V. Crew H 41, commanded by Lt H. A. Whittenbury, were the first to see action in 9199, now known by its Crew as No H 41, on 8th August 1918, at the start of the battle of Amiens. Lt Whittenbury describes the action in his Battle History Sheet.

Commenced the attack at 8.20 a.m. proceeding the Infantry by about 100 yds. …enemy gun flashes observed… Drove on zig-zag course… Both six pounders

A Heavy Mk V before moving into battle.

A Mark V of 2nd Battalion Tank Corps being passed by French artillerymen, towing captured German guns, in 1918. The crew relax having seen action during a successful attack on the village of Méaulte, on the Western Front.

had picked up targets and were firing… Drove down steep slope into ravine… opened fire with both six pounders firing 6 pdr (HE) and case shot at 40 yds range into the trenches and dugouts. Also fired a good many rounds with front Hotchkiss and observed many casualties.

At 10.15, after a fierce battle, H 41 returned unscathed from the battle having expended eighty-seven 6 pdr shot, eighteen case shot and 1,960 Hotchkiss rounds. Whittenbury was awarded a Military Cross for his gallant action. H 41 next saw action on 23rd August, when commanded by Lt T. J. DeCourcey, but saw little action that day apart from capturing an enemy machine-gun nest. Finally, on 29th September 1918, Commanded by Lt T. R. Harding, H 41 preceding the Infantry on attack on the village of Estrees, was hit and damaged by enemy shell fire. In his Battle History Sheet, Lt Harding writes:

Fire seemed to be coming from all directions… I moved forward… in the direction of Cabaret Wood and fired on a light field gun position there. Before I could come within near range my tank was hit near the left idle sprocket. …I was able to bring my tank to the Rallying Point but on arrival my left track broke and fell off.

From 1918-19, No: 9199 was used for training purposes and in 1921 went to 4th Battalion Tank Corps, at Wogret near Wareham, returning to Bovington in 1925. From this time until 1945 it was used for towing and recovery purposes by Tank Corps workshops and the Driving and Maintenance School.

It was donated to the Tank Museum by the Royal Armoured Corps Centre in 1949. Since that time T 9199 has been the centre of attraction at many Bovington Battle Days and was inspected by HM The Queen, leading the parade on 14th July 1967 at the Mounted Review of the Royal Tank Regiment in their 50th Anniversary year at Rheinsehlen Camp, BAOR, West Germany. Again, on 12th July 1985, H41 brought up the rear at the Standards Parade when HM The Queen presented new Standards to the Royal Tank Regiment in Sennelager, BAOR. On this occasion it was crewed by four members of the Museum staff, including the Curator's wife! Its next

run was on the seventieth anniversary of the Battle of Amiens, 8th August 1918, in which it fought. On this occasion one member of its crew was Mr Ted Wakefield, aged ninety-four, from Weymouth, who drove a Mark V in the same battle. In late 1990, it was again on the move, this time for Japanese TV. In one scene it was driven over a specially constructed trench with a cameraman in the bottom!

Tank crews of 8th Battalion Tank Corps talk to German prisoners and their guards before an attack on the Hindenburg Line. The tanks in the background are carrying cribs (a replacement of fascines), which were dropped from the front of the tank into a ditch before crossing.

SPECIFICATIONS

Manufacturer:	Birmingham Railway Carriage Co;
Pattern Date:	1917
Condition:	Runner (1990)
Engine:	Ricardo, 6-cylinder, petrol-fuelled, water-cooled, 150 bhp at 1200 rpm
Max Speed:	4.6 mph
Range:	45 miles.
Armour:	14-16mm.
Armament:	2 6 pounders (57mm); 4 .303 inch Hotchkiss machine-guns
Crew:	8 (commander, driver, 6 gunners)
Length:	26' 5"
Height:	8' 8"
Width:	13' 6"
Weight:	29 tons

Peerless Armoured Car
L1360

Owing to the demand for mechanical transport in the early stages of the Great War, the British Government purchased a large number of trucks from America. These were used, for the most part, as Anti Aircraft Gun Lorries and could be seen, on all British Fronts, throughout the war and proved very reliable.

At the end of the war, about one hundred of these lorries were converted into armoured cars. The type and shape of the armoured body was similar to the Austin Armoured Cars of 17th Tank Battalion in France, with twin turrets. The 5 ton lorry chassis was able to carry the extra weight of the armour and weapons without difficulty. The same solid tyres and chain drive was employed. These Armoured Cars, though heavy and slow (the road speed was governed to 10 mph), were fitted with an independent reverse steering column which was of considerable advantage in street warfare. They were also had two 40 Candle Power searchlights, one attached to the flap of each revolving turret. The wheels could be fitted with non-skid chains but the cars were too heavy and cumbersome to be used for cross country work.

Peerless Armoured Cars were used during the General Strike in the twenties, when their main role was to escort food convoys from the docks. They also saw service in Ireland during operations between 1920-22, some then being handed over to the Irish Free State Army.

The Museum's Peerless is displayed in the markings of 23rd Armoured Car Company, RTC, (Sharpshooters), the Sharpshooters being one of eight Yeomanry Regiments of the Territorial Army converted into RTC Armoured Car Companies in 1923. They were used for training and at annual camps, some still being in service

A Peerless armoured car of 23rd Armoured Car Company (Sharpshooters) TA on a public relation exercise, outside Brittannic House in London.

when World War Two began. It is believed that the Museum's Peerless was used as an Airfield Defence Vehicle at an airfield in Gloucestershire, certainly this was a role delegated to the remaining Peerless, along with Home Guard duties, during the early part of the War.

In the late eighties, two of the Museum's warding staff carried out some excellent restoration work to the woodwork, removing the years of green paint and polishing the wood to perfection. Although technically still a runner, this AFV has not been given an airing since 1967.

A convoy of Peerless armoured cars in front of the Admiralty Arch in Trafalgar Square, London, during the troubles of the Great Strike of 1926.

SPECIFICATIONS

Manufacturer:	Peerless Motor Co., Cleveland, Ohio. Converted into an armoured car by the Woolwich Arsenal Workshops.
Pattern Date:	1919
Condition:	runner (1967)
Engine:	Peerless, 4-cylinder, water-cooled, petrol-fuelled 40 bhp
Max. Speed:	18 mph (governed to 10 mph)
Range:	90 miles (144 km)
Armament:	2 Hotchkiss .303-inch machine-guns
Armour:	3 - 6 mm
Crew:	5
Length:	20'2"
Height:	8' 4"
Width:	7'4"
Weight:	6¾ tons

Renault FT 17
63168 PROTOTYPE

In December 1915, an artillery officer, Colonel Jean Baptiste Estienne (later dubbed the 'Father of the French Tank Corps'), requested an interview with General Joffre, the French Commander-in-Chief, in order to put forward his theories on the subject of mounted artillery on an armoured chassis. Having obtained agreement in principle, Estienne approached various companies and two, Schneider and F.A.M.H (Compagnie des Forges et Aciéries de la Marine et d'Homécourt), accepted the challenge. The former developed a medium weight tank, the 13½ ton Schneider, the latter the 23 ton St. Chamond. Early in 1916, each company received an order for 400 vehicles, the initial models being issued to the French Army in September 1916, just after the British had first used their tanks on the Somme. However, to complement these medium tanks, Estienne foresaw that there was a specialised role for a lighter vehicle to accompany the infantry. He approached Louis Renault, who had been one of the industrialists he had initially turned to but who had declined the challenge.

In 1916, when re-approached, he changed his mind and within a short time had been seized with enthusiasm for the light tank project. The first official trials of the Renault FT took place at Champlieu camp on 9th April 1917. They proved entirely satisfactory, the tank having excellent cross country abilities, climbing a 50-degree gradient and a 6-foot ditch. The Commité Consultatif gave their agreement for an order of 1,000 production models. The abbreviation 'FT' is often wrongly described

The FT 17 light tank, sometimes called the 'Inkpot' or Mosquito, had a very cramped driving position and only one man in the turret who was both commander and gunner.

U.S. OFFICIAL

The two-man crew stand by their vehicle. The skid-tail, which can be seen at the rear of the tank, was to improve its trench-crossing ability.

as standing for 'Failbe Tonnage', ie: light tank, however, it was in fact merely a factory product designation alloted by Renault to that particular type of vehicle.

The basic form of the FT 17 light tank was an armoured box thinned towards the rear, where the 35 bhp Renault engine was located. The petrol was pumped from two tanks with a combined capacity of 22 gallons. The transmission included Renault cone clutches and a Renault gearbox, with four forward and one reverse speeds. One of the most innovative features was the octagonal turret of eight armoured plates replacing the moulded steel turrets found on early models, which was mounted on a bearing race which the gunner could easily turn manually; this was the first example of a 360-degree, or fully-traversing turret. The tracks passed over extremely large front wheels, which projected well forward of the vehicle permitting it to cross the most difficult of terrain. This cross country ability was further enhanced by the 'Skid Tail' which gave the effect of increasing the track length, which was only 358cm (11 feet 9 inches) thus improving its trench crossing ability.

The battle for the Forest of Retz, on 31st May 1918, was the first engagement in which the FT 17 took part. This was during a crucial point in the great German summer offensive. The FT 17s, although only introduced in small numbers, performed well. On 18th July of the same year, 480 FTs were concentrated in the French counter-offensive at Soissons where, in the opening attack, they broke through the German line without artillery preparation. However their advance of four miles could not be exploited.

The FT 17, known unofficially in the British Tank Corps as the Inkpot or Mosquito tank, proved the most sucessful light tank of World War One and total production figures exceeded four thousand. Four main variants of the FT 17 were produced: the 7.92mm machine-gun tank; a 37mm gun tank, a 75mm gun tank; and a Signal tank. Of the 4,000 vehicles on order in February 1918, the breakdown was; 1,000 machine-gun tanks, 1,830 37mm gun tanks, 200 signal tanks and, finally, 970 75mm gun tanks.

Postwar, the success story continued, and a vast array of variants was produced including a Self-propelled 105mm gun tank, Searchlight tank, Fascine tank, FT Plough, FT Tractor, Bulldozer, Cargo Carrier, Amphibian and Bridgelayer. Apart from those built under license in the USA, they were exported from France to Belgium, Brazil, Canada, China, Spain, Finland, Japan, Holland, Poland and Chechoslovakia. In Italy, they developed the design and renamed it the Fiat 3000 and the Soviet Union recovered a number from the White Russian Armies and developed the MS-1.

The FT 17 was one of the few important tanks produced of which the Tank Museum had no model. So an exchange was arranged with the Imperial War Museum and on 13th May 1965, the Mosquito tank, FT 17 No 63168 arrived in Bovington. It is one of the first prototypes making it among the oldest FT 17 to survive. As it is a prototype it was built of unarmoured steel (see plate on the front marked 'non protege'). Unfortunately, the vehicle came with no information as to its history, and further research has, to date, revealed little. The engine and transmission was missing and to date a replacement has not been acquired.

SPECIFICATIONS

Manufacturer:	Louis Renault, Billancourt Seine, France.
Pattern Date:	1917
Condition:	non-runner
Engine:	Renault, 4-cylinder, petrol-fuelled, water-cooled, 40 bhp at 1500 rpm
Max. Speed:	6 kmph
Range:	24Kms
Armour:	6 - 22mm
Armament:	7.92mm Mitrailleuse automatique Hotchkiss Brevete.
Crew:	2 (commander/gunner, driver)
Length:	(incl. tail) 5.02m
Height:	2.18m
Width:	1.78m
Weight:	6¾ tons

Medium A (Whippet)
A 259 CAESAR II

Designed by Sir William Tritton in November 1916, the Medium A, also known as the "Tritton Chaser" or Whippet was the only medium tank to see action during the Great War. Construction began on 21st December 1916 at William Foster and Co Ltd, Lincoln and trials of the Whippet were held on 11th February 1917, after which an order for 200 was placed for June 1917.

The Whippet was run on two petrol-fuelled, water-cooled, four-cylinder Tylor J.B. 4 engines each of 45 bhp (one for each track), with dual ignition. It also had twin four-speed gearboxes and clutches, making it very difficult to handle and seriously increasing servicing time. Gentle steering on roads was by means of a column which controlled the throttle on each engine (and therefore each track), accelerating one and retarding the other automatically. For larger turns the gearboxes were used.

Seventy gallons of petrol was contained in a drum-shaped petrol tank placed horizontally in front of the machine in armour plating and was fed to the engine by the Autovac system. The tracks were half-round, reverting to the *Little Willie* type. Two towing shackles and hooks, and oak spuds were provided as there was no unditching gear. For observation, three rotary peephole covers and three periscope openings were provided. This type of vehicle was first used on 26th March 1918 at Hebuterne, Second Battle of the Somme.

The Museum's Whippet, *Caesar II; A253*, was attached to the 3rd (Light) Tank Battalion, Tank Corps, and was commanded by Lt Cecil Harold Sewell, No 9 Section, C Company, who was awarded the Victoria Cross for his gallant action in an attack at Frémicourt. From 21st March up to the middle of October 1918, the 3rd (Light) Tank Battalion had been engaged in both defensive and offensive operations, gaining such a reputation that no enemy infantry would face up to their Whippets. On 29th August during an attack at Frémicourt, Sewell and his section were ordered to clear up a nasty situation in which the advance of the 3rd New Zealand Rifle Brigade had been held up by heavy machine-gun fire. On advancing through the infantry Sewell and his tanks were met by heavy fire from enemy artillery and machine-guns. Whilst manoeuvring to avoid this fire, Whippet A233 commanded by Lt O. L. Rees-Williams side-slipped into a deep shell crater, turning turtle, trapping those inside, and catching fire. The official account of his action follows:

> This officer displayed the greatest gallantry and initiative in getting out of his own Tank and crossing open ground under heavy shell and machine-gun fire

A nice detail shot of a Medium A, new off the production line, outside the Lincoln factory of William Foster & Co. Ltd.

His Majesty King George V inspects Heavy tanks, Medium As and their crews in France. Curious onlookers can be seen on the treeline above.

to rescue the crew of another Whippet of his section which had side-slipped into a large shell hole, overturned and taken fire. The door of the Tank having become jammed against the side of the shell hole, Lieutenant Sewell, by his own unaided efforts dug away the entrance to the door and released the crew. In doing so he undoubtedly saved the lives of the officers and men inside the Tank, as they could not have got out without his assistance. After having extricated the crew, seeing one of his own men lying wounded behind the Tank, he again dashed across the open ground to his assistance. He was hit while doing so, but he succeeded in reaching the Tank, when a few minutes later he was again hit fatally in the act of dressing his wounded driver. During the whole of this period he had been in full view of, and at short range of enemy machine-gun and rifle pits, and throughout, by his prompt and heroic actions, showed utter disregard for his own personal safety.

His driver Gunner W. Knox, sadly also died from his wounds.

Shortly after this action, with the end of the war, *Caesar II* was brought back to Bovington and kept with the Tank Corps collection of tanks, which in 1923 officially became the RTC Museum. As mentioned on the brass plate, which can be seen on the vehicle, Sewell's Victoria Cross is also on display in the Museum.

SPECIFICATIONS

Manufacturer:	Foster & Co Ltd, Lincoln.
Pattern Date:	1916
Condition:	non-runner
Engine:	2 Tylor 45 bhp petrol-fuelled combined to give 90 bhp at 1,000 rpm
Max. Speed:	8.3 mph
Range:	max 80 miles
Armour:	5 - 14mm
Armament:	4 .303-inch Hotchkiss machine-guns
Crew:	3 (commander, driver, machine gunner)
Length:	20'
Height:	9'
Width:	8'7"
Weight:	14 tons

Carden Loyd Carrier Mk VI
No T 612
REG NO MT 9909

Shortly before the end of the Great War, the idea for a small, light, tracked vehicle, to act in a reconnaissance role for the heavy tanks, was proposed. The idea was conceived by Major G. le Q. Martel who produced a list of specifications:

a. It should be able to cross difficult terrain including any natural ditch or bank;
b. Road (or good, level ground) speed of 15 mph;
c. Cross country speed of 3-4 mph;
d. Climb a gradient of 1 in 1;
e. To use a production motor car engine of around 20 hp, (ordinary commercial spare parts could therefore be used);
f. Armoured against small arms and small calibre armour piercing bullets;
g. Armed with a light automatic weapon.

Martel himself made the first model which was demonstrated in 1925. However, independently of Martel, Sir John Carden and partner Vivian Loyd, were working towards similar goals.

In 1926, various Carden-Loyd and Morris-Martel prototype 'Tankettes' were examined. The Morris-Martel proved to be reliable and easy to maintain but the Morris Co. had other commercial interests, so Carden and Loyd were left to develop their ideas.

The Carden-Loyd Mk V1, first produced in 1927, was a great success, the culmination of many experimental ideas and trials. The engine and gearbox was from the Model T Ford, a proven commercial engine with sales worldwide for which spare parts were therefore easily available. On earlier models of Carden-Loyd, track life had been a problem but after experimentation this was solved by using a track of 'malleable cast iron with double guides.' The previous model, the Mark V, was a wheel-cum-track machine, which had a pair of large pneumatic tyred wheels at the sides for road use, but these were later abandoned. The Mark VI had two pairs of solid tyred road rollers on each side suspended on short leaf springs as part of its regular suspension.

It was a two man vehicle with driver on the left and gunner on the right, firing a .303" Vickers MG, sitting side by side. Although it originally evolved as a weapons

The Museum's Carden Loyd Mark VI, Regd No: MT 9905, whilst on trial with MWEE.

Carden Loyd Mk VI towing tracked troop carrier and machine gun.

carrier, it was invariably used for reconnaissance by the RTC until the development of suitable light tanks.

Large numbers were produced and many variants including mortar carriers and gun limbers. The Mark VI was simple, cheap and, with its low profile and centre of gravity, was both inconspicuous and almost impossible to tip over. The engine situated between the two crew was insulated with asbestos and the fuel tank, carrying ten gallons (sufficient for 100 miles), was behind them. This little vehicle was very agile. It had a top speed of 30 mph, could climb a vertical wall a little over a foot high, ford water of 2-feet in depth and had a turning circle of 13-feet.

The discussions surrounding the Mark VI made it one of the best known vehicles of its time and its design concept led to two lines of development: a machine-gun carrier for mechanised infantry, and a light tank for armoured reconnaissance. Its influence can also be seen in light vehicles from other countries, such as the French Renault Chenillette and the Italian CV3/35.

The Museum's Carden Loyd was restored to full running order by the staff in 1989-90. Certain modern parts had to be used, such as a radiator, whilst some sections of the steelwork were replaced. This was part of the Curator's deliberate policy to keep a suitable percentage of the collection in running order.

SPECIFICATIONS

Manufacturer:	Vickers Armstrong Ltd, Newcastle upon Tyne.
Pattern Date:	1928
Condition:	Runner (1991)
Engine:	Ford model T of 22.5 bhp
Max. Speed:	30 mph
Range:	100 miles
Armour:	bulletproof
Armament:	.303-inch Vickers machine-gun
Crew:	2
Length:	2.46 m (8'1")
Height:	1.22 m (4')
Width:	1.70 m (6'6")
Weight:	1.25 tons

Citröen-Kégresse P 10 Half Track
NO. 3461, REGISTRATION SM 7802

The first person to devise a half-track system was a French automotive engineer Adolphe Kegresse, whilst he was the manager of the Tsar of Russia's Imperial Automobile Service in 1917. He replaced the two driven rear wheels by short rubber tracks in order to overcome the problems of negotiating the terrible snow and mud of the Russian winters. His system was applied to some of the Austin armoured cars used by the Russian Army. However, he had to flee from the country after the revolution, returning to France, where his ideas were taken up by the Citroen Motor Company. Kegresse collaborated with Andreé Citroen who had entered the car manufacturing industry in 1919 – his 7.5 and 11.4 hp models were already renowned. They demonstrated the half track system developed by Kégresse on Citröen B-type cars, by driving over snowbound mountain roads in the winter and proved the possibility of traction over marshlands during the summer. The idea was then conceived by Andre Citröen to send a number of cars across the Sahara, proving the Kégresse systems ability, and military potential, to cross the most rugged and destructive terrain.

They started from Touggourt on 17th December 1922 and reached Timbuctoo, 2,025 miles (3,240 km) later, on 7th January 1923. They stayed a month before starting back on 9th February returning to their start point of Touggourt on 6th March. Due to the nature of some of the country and peoples they would pass, one of the vehicles was armed with three machine-guns. The cars, fully laden, weighed around two and a half tons and traveled at an average speed of between 9 and 11 mph. Petrol consumption was 10 miles per gallon (16 km/p/g).

The system was also used as the basis for several French armoured cars, the first 16 Citroen-Kegresse-Schneider half-track armoured cars were ordered by the French Army in 1923 and were followed by improved models, so that by 1930 there were some 100 half-tracks in service.

The vehicle in the museum, on loan from the the National Motor Museum, Beaulieu, originally belonged to the French Army. In 1936, it was purchased by the

A Citröen Kegresse at the Wool trials.

Her Majesty Queen Mary on a visit with the army in the late 1920s.

Duke of Buccleuch who lived at Drumlanrig Castle, Dumfries, who used it as a shooting brake. The registration book shows that it remained in the Duke's service until 1930. From 1930-36 little is known. The next record we have is when it came to the notice of Mr Clements, of East Knoyle, Wiltshire. He saw the vehicle being used by his neighbour to haul timber and, after many attempts, he sucessfully purchased it in 1946. He used it as an all weather, towing and recovery vehicle for many years. In the instruction book (written in English) the claim is made that the loads it can handle are:

On gradients not exceeding 8% … 5 tons. On gradients not exceeding 18% … 2½ tons. On gradients not exceeding 25% … 2 tons. On rails … 50 tons. On water (barge towing) … 1,000 tons.

The British Army purchased a number of models between 1924 and 1926, which were used as Staff Cars, Gun Tractors and Signal Line Layers. Kégresse tracks were also used by the British Army on their Crossley and Burford half-tracks.

SPECIFICATIONS

Manufacturer:	Citröen, Paris
Pattern date:	1925
Condition:	possible runner.
Engine:	Citröen 4-cylinder, 1,598 cc, petrol-fuelled, 11.4 hp
Max. Speed:	25 mph
Range:	unknown
Armour:	nil
Armament:	nil
Crew:	driver (3 passengers)
Length:	14′4″
Height:	5′9″
Width:	5′
Weight:	1.2 tons

Crossley Armoured Car Mk I, 6 x 4.
M 1035 / HX 6802

In the late 1920s, the RASC Training College, in conjunction with some British commercial vehicle manufacturers, developed a most successful form of driven rear bogie for six wheelers, which gave an unrivalled cross-country performance almost on a par with the half-track, which clearly had both military and civilian use, especially in underdeveloped countries. In its military application the Crossley 30 cwt BGV2 6 x 4 chassis was used.

In 1930, two experimental 6 x 4 models, D2E1 and D2E2, were produced with double rear wheels and cylindrical turrets. Later, five production cars were ordered. These had single rear tyres and the same turret as Light Tank Mk II (also on show in the Museum), fitted with the two Vickers .303-inch machine-guns and for improved cross country performance tracks could be fitted over the rear wheels. Only five were ever completed as the Army preferred light tanks, which were better powered and could cross rougher terrain.

The five cars were all used by the 12th Royal Lancers as squadron commanders cars in Egypt, 12 RL being one of the first cavalry regiments to be mechanised when they took over 3rd Armoured Car Company's Rolls Royces in 1929. Despite their extra wheels, overall tracks and unditching beams they proved too heavy for desert use as compared with the Rolls and were normally kept locked away in a hangar!

Crossley Mk V, 6 x 4 armoured car.

All five subsequently returned to UK where they were used for home defence and for training the newly forming regiments in the early part of World War Two.

The Crossley 6 x 4 in the Museum was thus used by various regiments, including 24th Armoured Car Company (Derbyshire Yeomanry), 11th Hussars and 12th Lancers. It was donated to the Museum in 1949 by the Royal Tank Regiment. In 1987 it was restored and repainted in the Museum workshops but problems with the thermo-syphon cooling system, which would not retain coolant, means that it cannot be used for mobile displays.

SPECIFICATIONS

Manufacturer:	Crossley Motors Ltd, Manchester. (Chassis)
	Royal Ordnance Factory, Woolich Arsenal. (Armour)
Pattern Date:	1931
Condition:	potential runner (cooling problems)
Engine:	Crossley 4 cylinder petrol fueled, water cooled, 58 bhp at 2600 rpm.
Max. Speed:	50 mph (touring 35/40 mph)
Range:	120 miles
Armour:	6 - 9mm
Armament:	2 .303-inch Vickers machine-guns
Crew:	3 (Commander, driver, gunner, hull gunner)
Length:	15' 4" (4.65m)
Height:	7' 10½" (2.36m)
Width:	6' 3" (1.88m)
Weight:	5.5 tons

Independent A1E1
T1020

In December 1922, the War Office asked Vickers to prepare outline drawings for a new heavy tank to replace the World War One Mark V. The outline specifications dictated that it was to have a speed of 7 mph, to climb a 30 degree slope, cross a 9-foot trench, have a ground clearance of 18 inches, a ground pressure of 12 lb/sq in and sinkage of 3 inches, and finally it should be armed with a 3 pdr and two .303-inch machine-guns. The War Office envisaged that the highest point of the tank should be the cover over the driver's head. The 3 pdr gun was to be mounted at the side of the driver firing between the horns, giving it an arc of fire of only 30 degrees (approximately). The machine-guns were to be mounted in sponsons and capable of 180 degrees arc of fire to cover front and rear of the tank.

By 13th March, two schemes were put forward, the first following the lines envisaged by the War Office, except that four machine-guns were provided for, one at each corner of the vehicle. The second scheme placed the main gun in an all-round traversing turret on top of the hull and the machine-guns in four small separate turrets with limited traverse only. This brought the overall height up to 8 feet 9 inches and the weight to 25 tons 7 cwts, an increase in weight which had to be balanced against the inherent advantage of all-round traverse of the main weapon. By the end of April 1923, both proposals were ready for consideration by the General Staff Tank Committee. Eventually, the latter design was decided to be the most effective (keeping track of all the weapons was so difficult, that later indicators were fitted to show the direction the weapons were pointing in, relative to the tank's centre line). The overall concept having been settled, work was then concentrated on details of the design. It was decided that only one vehicle should be built, at this time, financed from the £40,000 available for experimental work in 1924.

As its name suggests, *Independent* was intended to work alone, destroying enemy

An excellent close up shot of Independent.

Independent, A6E2 16 ton medium tank (known as the 16 Tonner) and Light Tank Mark I.

tanks and exploiting breakthroughs. On 10th July 1924, the first of a long series of detailed design meetings was held. Over the next year meetings were held to discuss every detail of *Independent* design. On 26th February 1925 for example, at a meeting attended by Mr Siddeley of Armstrong-Siddeley, it was decided that the tank should be powered by a 350 bhp air-cooled V12 engine running at 1500 rpm (originally the engine was to have been 120 hp). This, it was anticipated would give it a speed of 20 mph. The final specifications were decided upon on 21st July 1925 and in the same month the War Office told Vickers that financial sanction had been given for the manufacture of the tank. The pilot model was delivered to the Mechanical Warfare Experimental Establishment in 1926.

In many respects this design was a great advance in the evolution of the modern tank; the eight-man crew used laryngaphones to communicate, the controls were hydraulically operated and steering was by wheel, except for sharp turns. The armament consisted of a Quick Firing Semi-Automatic (QFSA) 3 pdr gun (47 mm) in the main turret and four auxiliary turrets, each mounting a water-cooled .303-inch machine-gun, one of which could be used in an anti-aircraft role. Only one prototype was built and this underwent stringent and extensive trials. It made its public debut at the Dominion Premiers' Demonstration at Camberley on 13th November 1926, when it was classified as top secret and got a lot of press coverage.

Unfortunately the design of *Independent* was ahead of the technology needed to build it and many problems arose. This was not helped by the fact that the actual weight of the completed vehicle was over 7 tons heavier than originally specified, at 32 tons, and a heavy tank with a top speed of 20 mph was moving into entirely new territory. The air-cooled V12 engine proved extremely heavy on oil consumption and was notoriously difficult to start. The rubber tyres of the road wheels, the brakes, the engine, the final drive and the suspension all gave trouble. The tank was really too long for its width, which made it difficult to steer, and this caused major problems at the rear, where the track frames started to peel away from the hull. In 1928, after consultations with W.G. Wilson, the final drive was entirely rebuilt, including a new spoked, self-cleaning drive sprocket. To get over the starting problem it was fitted with an aero-marine inertia starter, an American device which was used on Greyhound buses.

Numerous tests and trials were held and a plethora of faults were discovered and corrected. Unfortunately, after seven years of trials, the project was abandoned due to its high cost of £150,000! In spite of this, *Independent* turned out to be of the greatest experimental value, breaking new ground in many fields, for example, it was the first tank to have a co-axial machine-gun, and new inroads were made into crew comfort and safety. The influence of the design features of *Independent* can be seen in the Russian T35 and T38 and the French 'Char de Rupture'.

All the work was undertaken under the strictest secrecy but *Independent* indirectly became the centre of attention during the notorious Baillie-Stewart affair. At the time of its trials, the German General Staff showed great interest and in 1932 Lt Norman Baillie-Stewart, of the Seaforth Highlanders, was arrested and charged with selling secrets to a German Army major. He was held in detention for nine weeks in the Tower of London, the last Briton to have that dubious honour, before his trial at the Old Bailey. He was found guilty, cashiered and sentenced to five years imprisonment. In 1937, having been released from jail, Baillie-Stewart moved to Austria, took out German Citizenship and joined the German Propaganda Ministry just before the start of War in 1939. He made English-language broadcasts at the beginning of the war, until his job was taken over by William Joyce, the infamous Lord Haw-Haw, who was later hung. Finally, in 1946, he was again held for trial at the Old Bailey where he was sentenced to five years imprisonment for 'aiding the King's enemies'. Throughout this episode Baillie-Stewart professed that he was a victim of circumstance and had acted innocently and in good faith. He states in his book (in which he attempts to clear his name):

Another feature of the case is that if I had been given secret information about the new British light tank, I would have required a blueprint... or a photograph. There was never any evidence or suggestion that I had either. A picture of the outside of the tank had appeared in the public Press.

There is, however, some doubt as to whether the *Independent* was actually the tank at the centre of the Baillie-Stewart saga. As can be seen in the excerpt from Baillie's book above, he speaks of a 'light' tank and certainly David Fletcher, our Librarian, is now convinced that it was the Sixteen Tonner which was the vehicle concerned and not the A1E1.

Although rejected by the army *Independent* did see service eventually, when it was removed from the Museum during World War Two to guard the approaches to Bovington.

SPECIFICATIONS

Manufacturer:	Vickers Armstrong Ltd, Newcastle upon Tyne.
Pattern Date:	1926
Condition:	non-runner
Engine:	Armstrong Siddeley, air-cooled, V-12, 398 bhp at 1600 rpm
Max. Speed:	25 mph
Range:	95 miles
Armour:	20mm - 25mm
Armament:	3 pounder, 47mm, QFSA gun .303 inch machine-gun
Crew:	8 (commander, driver, gunner, loader, 4 machine gunners).
Length:	25'6"
Height:	9'
Width:	9'
Weight:	32 tons

Leyland 6 x 4 Armoured Car
ZC 774

After the foundation of the state of Eire in 1922, the Irish Army had received a number of armoured vehicles from the departing British forces. These included Rolls-Royce and Peerless armoured cars and Lancia armoured lorries. Four of the Peerless ACs were unserviceable and so the 13 Rolls-Royces made up the 'Armoured Squadron'.

With no prospects of additional vehicles or parts for the existing obsolete vehicles, the then Acting Director of the Cavalry Corps, Commandant J. V. Lawless submitted a memo to his superiors;

> The idea was that some suitable commercial chassis, preferably of a make and type already in general use in the country, should be selected. A suitable armoured hull… could be rapidly fitted… with a minimum of alterations. …I went on to suggest that I was prepared to transfer the hull of one of the (now unserviceable) Peerless cars if a TE 2 Leyland six-wheel chassis were purchased…

Throughout the 1930s, armies tended towards building armoured cars by armouring existing 6 x 4 truck chassis, *e.g.* the Russians did this with their Gaz BA-10m, the Japanese with the type 2592 and the Italians with the Fiat 611/Ansaldo, and of course the British Crossley and Lanchester, both of which are on show in the Museum. The Irish Army used Lawless' idea, based on the 6 x 4 Leyland Terrier chassis, purchased from Ashenhurst of Dublin in 1934, and using armour salvaged from obsolete British Peerless ACs. The first Leyland armoured car was built in 1934, but due to various modifications, *e.g.* the addition of a turret, it was not completed until May 1938.

In all, four armoured cars of this type were produced in Cavalry Workshops in the Curragh Camp, and they were taken into service by July 1939, being allocated the registration numbers ZC 773–ZC 776. ZC 774, the Leyland in the museum, was

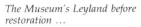

The Museum's Leyland before restoration …

completed between May 1938 and July 1939. They were powered by a six-cylinder Leyland engine and sported a L60 light tank turret, supplied by the Swedish firm of Landsverk (cf: L 180 armoured car also in Irish Army service). The car entered service with 1st Armoured Squadron, which was disbanded in May 1940 and in 1942 the Leylands joined a Heavy Armoured Squadron.

In 1955, Colonel Lawless returned to the Cavalry Corps as Director and arranged for the Leylands to have new Ford V-8 engines fitted. While this was being done the opportunity was taken to re-design the front of the hull along the lines of the Landswerk L 180. ZC 774's engine was re-fitted between January and October 1958, when the front was also modified. The four Leylands served with the re-established 1st Armoured Squadron until 1972, when the three surviving cars joined 5th Motor Squadron. They ended their service with 11th Cavalry Squadron (FCA) in Castlebar. Although obsolete by the end of the war the Leylands proved to be very reliable and easily maintained. ZC 774 was exchanged with the Irish Cavalry for a Ferret Mk 2/7 scout car in 1986, which can still be seen at their museum at the Curragh.

Following its arrival at Bovington, ZC 774 was fully restored by the Museum's conservation staff, including all its paintwork.

SPECIFICATIONS

Manufacturer:	Leyland Motors, Lancashire, Landsverk AB, Sweden (Turret) Irish Cavalry Workshops (Modifications)
Pattern Date:	1934
Condition:	runner
Engine:	Ford V-8 317, petrol-fueled, 155 bhp at 3200 rpm
Max. Speed:	45 mph
Range:	not known
Armour:	13 mm
Armament:	20mm Madsen cannon and 2 x Browning machine-gun
Crew:	4 (commander, driver, gunner, loader)
Length:	6.37m
Height:	2.43m
Width:	2.20m
Weight:	13 tons

Light Tank No 3 Amphibious L1E3
T2430

Of all the natural physical obstacles that it is possible to select for protection against attack by tanks, none is so effective as deep water, either by sea, lake, river or canal.

Amphibious tank development started after the Great War in 1919, when an amphibious version of the Mark IX was developed. Later, in 1921, a Medium D was modified to make it amphibious and then known as the Medium D**. It was used in trials which took place at Christchurch.

In 1930, Vickers-Armstrong took up the idea of producing an armed amphibious tank and produced two experimental models, given the War Office designation A4E11 and A4E12. The Vickers-Carden-Loyd A4E11 was described in *Meccano Magazine*:

It possesses all the fighting qualities of the latest type of light tank, and in addition is able to cross wide stretches of deep water as easily as it can cross the roughest country… its swimming efficiency is very high. Tests made in the

An overhead view of L1E3 before restoration.

River Thames just above Chertsey Lock, for instance, have shown that it is capable of crossing the full width of the river across the current without any loss of direction.

Though the British Army never bought anymore, sales abroad went well and models were sent to China, the Dutch East Indies, Thailand and the USSR, who later developed their own amphibious vehicle from this design.

Later, in 1939, an improved version, the L1E3, was developed. It was fitted with a Vickers .303-inch machine-gun in a rotating turret, as its armament, and 9mm bulletproof plate armour for protection (back and sides were only 7mm armour plate). The road wheels were drum-shaped to increase buoyancy and bouyancy tanks made from balsa wood, or kapok, encased in sheet steel were fitted to the watertight hull. In its amphibious role, it was propelled by twin propellers driven off the sprocket drive shafts. It was steered by cowls over the two propellers linked to the steering levers.

In June 1939, it was sent to the Mechanical Experimental Establishment where it was put through extensive trials. The cross country performance was good, the L1E3 could easily surmount a 45-degree slope, climb a 1-foot 8-inch high wall and cross a ditch 5 feet wide with vertical banks. The tank's water speed was around 3½-4 mph. After flotation tests in the Basingstoke canal, MEE reported:

The performance of this…machine is satisfactory and it has proved reliable over a mileage of 1,168. There appears to be adequate buoyancy and very little water gains access when afloat.

Although highly manoeuvrable in the water, its general performance was spoilt by the need to save weight.

However, the British Army did not take up the idea and the tank was returned

Amphibious tank L1E3 is easily recognisable due to the ribbed armour covering the balsa and kapok flotation tanks. Note also the twin screws at the rear.

to Vickers-Armstrong in February 1941. After the war, in November 1946, it was again sent to MEE, now known as MWEE, for further trials and then in September 1947 was handed over to the Military College of Science, Fighting Vehicles Wing, and subsequently lodged at the Tank Museum.

SPECIFICATIONS

Manufacturer:	Vickers Armstrong, Newcastle upon Tyne.
Pattern date:	1939
Condition:	non-runner
Engine:	Meadows, 6-cylinder, water-cooled, petrol-fueled, developing 89 bhp at 3,500 rpm.
Max. Speed:	land 30 mph (48.25 kmph) water 3-4 mph (5.95 kmph)
Range:	120 miles
Armour:	8 - 9 mm
Armament:	.303-inch Vickers machine-gun
Crew:	3 (commander, driver, gunner)
Length:	4.59 m (15'0)
Height:	2.31 m (7'7")
Width:	2.34 m (7'8")
Weight:	4.67 tons

Light Tank Mk VI B
T4149
HMC 547

British light and medium tank development began with the 'Whippet' which was created to provide a fast cavalry or pursuit tank to exploit any opportunity or break-through by the heavy tanks. Later, after the war, light tanks or tankettes were built to help mechanize the infantry. However, with the advent of these small, fast and low silhouette vehicles, a new concept for their use was found, namely to provide reconnaissance for the heavier tanks. Turreted versions of the Carden Loyd were developed and known as Patrol Tanks Marks I & II.

During the mid-thirties, Vickers-Armstrong spent much time and effort in the development of light tanks, through a series of two-man machines (Mks I to IV) mounting a single Vickers machine-gun, which were later enlarged into three man

The Museum's Light Mk VIB being crewed by members of the Society of Friends of the Tank Museum, during a Battle Day rehearsal at Gallows Hill.

light tanks armed with two machine-guns in a two-man turret. The first of these vehicles to enter service, developed from these experimental prototypes, was the light tank Mk V. It had a two-man turret, mounting both .303-inch and .50-inch machine-guns, and a much larger fighting chamber in the hull from earlier models, so as to be able to carry an observer or tank commander as well as the machine-gunner.

The Light Tank Mark VI, was similar to the Mark V except for its turret. This was redesigned to allow room for a wireless. There were various versions, the main two being the Marks VIA and VIB. The Mark VIA had a single return roller removed from the top of the leading bogie and attached to the hull sides, and an octagonal cupola fitted with two lookouts. The differences in the Mark VIB were to simplify production and included a one-piece armoured louvre over radiator (rather than two piece) and a plain circular commander's cupola, replacing the faceted one of the Mark V1A, fitted with glass block lookouts.

The Light Tank Mk VI series entered production in 1936 and a thousand were in service worldwide with the British Army at the outbreak of war. In 1940, both in Europe and North Africa, the Light Mark V1 formed a major part of British tank strength, when the British Expeditionary Force (BEF) sailed for France in 1940, they were to be found in all divisional cavalry regiments and in the cavalry light tank regiments of 1st Armoured Division. Unfortunately, it was used widely in roles other than that for which it was designed – reconnaissance – and, when used in a front line role, it often resulted in heavy losses when up against the better armed and armoured German tanks. However, the Mark V1 fought with distinction not only in France, but in the Western Desert, Greece, Malta, Crete, Syria (with the Australians) and took part in the siege of Tobruk.

The Mark VIB on the Bovington training area.

The Tank Museum's vehicle was used as a training vehicle at Bovington Camp during World War Two and has been kept in good running order ever since, taking part in numerous Battle Days and other events. In 1991 it was one of the six AFVs which took part in the Royal Tournament and ran during every performance. It is badged up for the 4th/7th Royal Dragoon Guards when they were serving in 2nd Infantry Division of the BEF in France in 1940.

SPECIFICATIONS

Manufacturer:	Vulcan Foundry, Newton le Willows.
Pattern Date:	1938
Condition:	runner (1975)
Engine:	Meadows, 6-cylinder, water-cooled, 85 bhp
Max. Speed:	34 mph
Range:	125 miles
Armour:	4 - 15mm
Armament:	15 mm BESA and 7.92 mm BESA machine-guns
Crew:	3
Length:	4.04 m (13'2")
Height:	2.26 m (7'5")
Width:	2.08 m (6'10")
Weight:	5.2 tons

Renault Chenillette d'Infantrie, Type UE
88371

The French Renault Chenillette was derived from the Carden-Loyd Mark VI and, in similar fashion, the engine and gearbox were between the crew who sat with their heads protected by armoured covers. It was used by the French Army, from 1931 onwards, mainly as a supply tractor. The stores were transported in the open rear compartment but, as this could not carry very much, a tracked trailer was usually towed on the back – which could carry up to 500 kg (1,102 lb) of extra

British soldiers try out a Chenilette in France, on 12th June 1944, shortly after D-Day.

A Chenilette converted by the Germans, to carry a 3.7cm PaK 35/36.

equipment. It was also used as a gun tractor, towing a 25mm A-T gun and a small number were armed with machine-guns and used by infantry combat units. In all, 6,700 was built, at first by Renault then, later, by Fouga, AMX and Berliet.

Following the French armistice of June 1940, they were taken over by the Germans. Their designation was Infantrie Schlepper UE 630(f) and the German Army used them as internal or airport security vehicles, munition carriers (Gepanzerter Munitionsschlepper UE (f)) and armed small numbers with PaK 35/36 3.7 cm anti-tank guns. A considerable number was issued to the Panzerpionier companies in France during 1943-44, armed with four Wurfrahmen 40 rockets to give increased bombardment potential. They were also used as a mobile mount for a wooden dummy tank!

The Museum's Chenillette was one of a batch tested by MWEE before the war and was probably used for training by the Free French in the UK.

SPECIFICATIONS

Manufacturer:	Societé Anonyme Usine Renault, Billancourt.
Pattern Date:	1931
Condition:	non-runner
Engine:	Renault 4-cylinder, water-cooled petrol-fueled, 38 bhp at 2,800 rpm.
Max. Speed:	30 mph
Range:	180 km
Armour:	4 - 7 mm
Armament:	nil
Crew:	2
Length:	2.80 m
Height:	1.25 m
Width:	1.74 m
Weight:	2 tons

Rolls-Royce Armoured Car Mk I
REGISTRATION NO H3830, 1920 PATTERN,
WAR DEPARTMENT NO M247.

This old warrior served with many different regiments all over the world. H3830 was first issued to the 5th Armoured Car Company (ACC), Royal Tank Corps (RTC), at Marlborough Barracks, Dublin, in January 1921. It served in Ireland until 1922 on escort and curfew duties and was well liked by those who served with it, especially as it replaced the old, slow Austin.

As with the 1914 pattern Rolls-Royce Armoured Car, the 1920 pattern was a Silver Ghost. The engine was practically the same except for some general improvements: aluminium alloy pistons replaced the cast iron ones; a self-starter was incorporated (operating through the gearbox); the cylinder walls were specially treated to reduce wear; the radiator doors were fitted with louvres to keep down the temperature when in action, and a mechanically driven air pump had been fitted, for the benefit of the crew; steel disc wheels replaced the wire-spoked pattern.

5th ACC then moved to Scarborough, taking its Rolls-Royces, until 1927, when they were transferred to Shanghai. There they served under the colours of the British Contingent of the League of Nations' International Force. Mechanist Sergeant Harry Mansfield who was with 5th ACC throughout this time tells how additional protection was added to the Rolls whilst in Shanghai:

> Owing to inadequate protection in the turret to the gunner's head, additional small turrets were fitted......they were called, for want of a better name 'Top Hats'. Also to stop natives from climbing aboard high tension electric devices were fitted.

A typical incident is described in 5th ACC Historical Records:

> At about 20.00 hrs on 21st March, 1927, Lt T. R. Newman MC, DCM with 1 sub-section was patrolling Darroch Rd from the direction of the Public School, the leading car being about 20-25 yds ahead of the 2nd car. After passing barrier 'A' the leading car found barrier 'B' was closed. At the same time heavy fire

The 'Garage' in Shanghai provided cover for all the Rolls-Royce armoured cars belonging to 5th ACC.

was opened on the car from the second storey of house 'C' and from the door of house 'D', the three O.R's [other ranks] of the crew being wounded almost immediately, the bullets entering the observation slots of the armoured car... Fire was returned on both Machine Guns... meanwhile Lt Newman in the leading car ordered two of the wounded men to evacuate... keeping the wounded driver and himself working the gun. The car then charged the gate of the barrier 'B' in the hope of breaking through but was unsucessful. The car was therefore backed towards the barrier 'A', the rear of the car passing through the gate but the front wheels caught in the post and wire entanglement. Lt Newman opened the door... to see, and received a bullet in the wrist. He then got out and went to the second car to get the car commander to extricate the car... whilst talking to him he again received a bullet in the same wrist about an inch from the former wound. ...On examination ... 91 hits were counted on the Armoured car, besides rents in the wings through which it was impossible to judge how many bullets had passed.

A convoy of Rolls-Royce armoured cars, of various models, during driver training at Wool. The photograph is taken from outside the Black Bear Inn looking towards what is now the Spar and Post Office in the main street.

From Shanghai H 3830 was then shipped to Egypt where it served with the 5th ACC, RTC from 1929-1932. In 1932, however, the 5th ACC were re-equipped with light tanks so the Rolls was handed over to the 12th Royal Lancers (Prince of Wales) and on their departure to the United Kingdom it went to the 11th Hussars (Prince Albert's Own), as they arrived in Egypt to relieve 12th Royal Lancers. They then upgraded to the Morris AC9 and the Rolls was shipped back to the United Kingdom and was issued to the 1st Derbyshire Yeomanry in 1939.

During the early month of World War Two, it was used for anti-invasion patrols along the North-East Coast. With the re-equipment of the 1st Derbyshire Yeomanry, in 1940, it was again transferred this time to the Driving & Maintenance School at the Army AFV School (later to become the Royal Armoured Corps Centre), Bovington.

In 1946, when the Royal Armoured Corps Tank Museum was being re-established after the end of the war, it was handed over as a museum exhibit. At present, it can be seen as it was during its time in Shanghai, in 1927, as one of the four cars of No 4 section, 5th ACC under the command of Lt G. W. Richards MC.

For many years the Museum's Rolls-Royce was, mistakenly, assumed to be *Wedding Bells*, the famous India pattern armoured car which had served in France (1914), Egypt (1916), Palestine (1917), Iraq (1918), South Russia (1919) and all over India from 1921 to 1940. Unfortunately, it has since been discovered that, despite strenuous efforts to save the historic old car, it was broken up in Ahmednagar in 1940, so all that now remains are parts of the clutch controls and radiator badge which have been made into a cigarette lighter (on show in the Museum).

The Rolls remains in immaculate order and has just undergone a complete overhaul and repainting, following its appearance at the 1991 Royal Tournament, where it ran in the arena during every performance. It has also been fitted with a new stainless steel exhaust system. Its colour scheme is now back to show how it would have looked in RTC service in UK in the thirties.

SPECIFICATIONS

Manufacturer:	1920 Rolls-Royce, Derby. Bodywork, Royal Ordnance Factories.
Pattern Date:	1920 Mk I
Condition:	runner (1991)
Engine:	Rolls-Royce 6-cylinder, water-cooled, 40/50 bhp.
Max. Speed:	60 mph (touring 35-40 mph)
Range:	150 miles
Armour:	6.5 - 8.5 mm
Armament:	1 Vickers .303-inch machine-gun.
Crew:	4
Length:	16' 7"
Height:	8'
Width:	6' 3½"
Weight:	4 tons unladen

Vickers Armstrong 6 ton Type B
VAE 1985

The Vickers-Armstrong Six-ton Tank was first produced in 1928 and came in two basic variants, the Type A with two separate, partly traversing turrets, each armed with a Vickers machine-gun; and the Type B armed with a single turret fitted with a 47mm quick firing gun and a coaxial Vickers machine-gun. In the Type B, the weapons were both mounted on 'a common trunnion axis' (ie: coaxially mounted). This Duplex mount meant that they were traversed and elevated together. As a result, the gunner had the option of either weapon, depending on whether he was dealing with personnel ('soft' targets) or armour ('hard' targets).

Although rejected by the British Army, great interest was shown in the 6 Ton Tank from abroad. Export orders included Bolivia, Bulgaria, China, Estonia, Finland, Greece, Japan, Poland, Portugal, Romania, Russia and Siam. It became a major source of ideas and influence in design on those who purchased it. The Russian T26 and

A line of 6 ton Mk Es in Finland. Twenty-seven vehicles were delivered to the Finns, by 1939.

Polish 7TP series, both copies of the 6 Ton built under licence, were the foundation of their countries' tank forces and many features were also copied in the American Light Tank T1, prototype of the M1/M3 series.

Though too light for the British Army, the 6 tonner was a credit to its designers, as proved by its popularity abroad. It was simple mechanically, well armed and armoured for its size and weight and relatively cheap and easy to produce. Strangely, although the British Army never actually ordered any 6 tonners, they took over a number built for other countries and used them for training purposes throughout the war, as was the case with the Museum's exhibit. It was one of four built for Siam in 1940, which were impounded and then used for home defence and training. Its hull form is somewhat different from the original six tonners, having an enlarged fighting compartment and smaller engine section. It has now been painted in the strange and rather garish camouflage pattern as used by Vickers Armstrong's during the inter-war period for their export models.

SPECIFICATIONS

Manufacturer:	Vickers Armstrong Ltd
Pattern Date:	1930
Condition:	non-runner
Engine:	Armstrong Siddeley, 4-cylinder, air-cooled. 87 bhp
Max. Speed:	22 mph
Range:	100 miles
Armour:	5 - 14 mm
Armament:	3 pounder (47mm) QFSA gun and .303-inch Vickers machine-gun
Crew:	3
Length:	4.57 m (15')
Height:	2.19 m (7'2")
Width:	2.41 m (7'11")
Weight:	8 tons

Vickers Medium Mk II*
T199/ML 8642

The first Model of the Vickers Medium, the Mk I, delivered to the British Army in 1923, was the first British tank, in service, to have a 360-degree traversing turret and geared elevation for the Quick Firing 3 pdr, main gun. The Mk II had many similarities with the Mk I, as the same chassis, engine and armament were used. Both also used the sprung 'box bogie' suspension which gave the Mk I a speed of 25-30 mph, far in advance of its theoretical design speed of around 15 mph. However, the extra weight of the Mk II reduced the top speed to around 13 mph. Armament comprised the 3pdr gun, plus two Vickers machine-guns in the hull sides and three Hotchkiss sticking out around the turret.

There were other differences between the Marks. Externally, the Mk IIs appeared much bulkier, the armour was thicker, the superstructure was a little higher, and the driver's hood stood proud of the hull top. Also, the driver's glacis was steeper, the headlights larger and the Mk IIs had suspension skirts. The major mechanical difference was in the steering, the Mk I having epicyclic steering and the Mk II having Rackham Steering (Major J.G. Rackham was one of the 1914-1918 war design staff who is also well known for his association with AEC), with an additional epicyclic gearbox between the main gearbox and the differential cum cross-shaft.

In 1925, deliveries began of the Vickers Medium Mk II, and 100 were supplied in all. They were still in service with training regiments in the early stages of World War Two. The Russians bought fifteen Mk IIs, dubbed by them the 'British Workman', for training purposes, although in 1941 they were reputed to have seen action on the Finnish Front.

In 1932, modifications were made to the Medium Mk II, resulting in the Marks II* and II**. In the former, the three Hotchkiss in the turret were replaced by a single

Vickers Mediums on manoeuvres.

56

A close up of the Medium Mk II. Of interest here are the tracks, which are still very basic in design.

coaxial Vickers, while the commander's cupola was set further back in the turret roof. A lead counterweight was added at the back of the turret. In the latter, the wireless was placed in an armoured container and attached at the back of the turret.

The Museum's Medium is a Mark II* (one star), which served with the 55th Training Regiment, Royal Tank Corps (the Royal Tank Corps became the Royal Tank Regiment in 1939 on the formation of the Royal Armoured Corps), during the early part of World War Two. Before that date it could have served with any of the home tank battalions. A total of 160 Mediums were built and before the war they played a major role in tactical experiments with armoured formations, both at home and abroad. They were, for example, in service with the 6th Battalion RTC in the Middle East, where a number were fitted with external asbestos cladding in an attempt to reduce the heat inside, during a series of tests in 1935-36. They continued to be used for training after war was declared, but never saw action. Latterly they were buried up to their turrets at Mersa Matruh as static pillboxes, being finally dug up by the Australians.

The Museum's Mk II* was restored to running order by Vickers Defence Systems in their Newcastle factory during the early eighties and drove into its current position in the Inter War Years Hall, but has not been run since.

SPECIFICATIONS

Manufacturer:	Royal Ordnance Factory, Woolwich.
Pattern Date:	1926
Condition:	runner (1984)
Engine:	Armstrong Siddeley V8 air-cooled, petrol-fueled, 90 bhp.
Max. Speed:	15 mph
Range:	120 miles
Armour:	6.25 - 8 mm
Armament:	3 pdr QFSA; 3 Vickers machine-guns
Crew:	5
Length:	5.33 m (17'6")
Height:	3.04 m (10'0")
Width:	2.78 m (9'1½")
Weight:	13.5 tons

Vickers Wheel-Cum-Track D3E1
T839, ML 8719

Track wear had been a problem since the very first tanks were designed and it was still a major design problem after the Great War ended. The tracks of the Heavy Mk I had a life of around fifty miles, by which time they were so stretched as to make further use impossible. Wear from the abrasive properties of the mixture of water and sand or dirt on the battlefield also caused considerable problems, which lubrication on its own could not surmount.

To circumvent the problem Vickers came up with a novel solution. In 1926, they modified a Medium Mk I tank to run on either wheels or tracks at a moment's notice, the system taking power from the gearbox to raise or lower the wheels, thus lifting the tracks. The theory was that for driving distances on surfaced roads, the wheels would be lowered, lifting the tracks from contact with the ground, thus saving track wear. In trials this proved unsatisfactory as the balance of the vehicle was upset, which resulted in pitching and a very rough ride.

In 1927, another experimental vehicle was built, based on the Wolsey standard truck chassis and armoured by Vickers. It combined a high road speed of 25 mph with good cross country tracked performance of 15 mph. However, it never got past the prototype stage.

In 1928, the Vickers wheel-cum-track (D3E1) was built. It was different from the Medium Mk I version in that the wheel suspension was rigidly attached to the hull and the track frames were mounted in vertical guides, so the tracks could be raised and lowered rather than the wheels. Inside it was a mechanical nightmare, separate drives having to be taken off the gearbox to power the rear wheels, or the tracks, or the track raising gear! When on its tracks it pitched violently as the tracks were too short. On wheels it was equally difficult to handle due to the long wheelbase, while the combination of narrow, solid tyres and brakes only on the rear wheels, made it very dangerous on roads. Two models were produced, one with turrets and one without, but no armament was ever fitted to either.

The Museum's wheel-cum-track was delivered by Vickers on 12th May 1928 to MWEE (ordered 9 June 27, contract no: T6508). On 19th October 1933 it was handed over to the RTC Centre and in 1949 was accessed into the Museum's collection.

Vickers Wheel-cum-track D3E1, with tracks up for road travel.

Tracks down for cross country driving.

SPECIFICATIONS

Manufacturer:	Vickers Armstrong Ltd
Pattern Date:	1928
Condition:	non-runner
Engine:	Armstrong Siddeley V-8 petrol-fuelled, air-cooled, 90 bhp
Max. Speed:	45 mph (wheels) 15 mph (tracks)
Range:	260mls (on wheels), 120mls (on tracks)
Armour:	5 - 8 mm
Armament:	2 Vickers machine-guns
Crew:	3
Length:	18'
Height:	9'
Width:	8'
Weight:	8.4 tons

Boarhound Armoured Car (T18E2)
F 205188

In 1940, the type of warfare taking place in the Western Desert between the British and Commonwealth troops on the one hand and the Italians on the other, meant that vast distances needed to be patrolled and reconnoitred. Tanks were clearly innappropriate for this role, whereas armoured cars with their greater radius of action, speed and more comfortable suspension (important on such long journeys) were ideal and were widely used by both sides. With the arrival of the Deutsches Afrika Korps even larger armoured cars were employed, the big eight wheeled Schwerer Panzerspahwagen Sd Kfz 231 and Sd Kafz 233 being used to great effect. Undoubtedly their effectiveness influenced Allied thinking, especially that of the British, who opted for larger and more powerful armoured cars.

In 1941, in the United States a development programme was initiated around British battle experience to produce medium and heavy wheeled vehicles. Specifications included armour of up to 1½ inches for the medium and 2 inches for the heavy and both were to be armed with a 37mm gun in a 360-degree rotating turret. The medium vehicle evolved into the T 17 Staghound and the heavy into the T 18 Boarhound.

The Yellow Truck and Coach Co., a subsidiary of General Motors, submitted a tender for the heavy vehicle, with an eight-wheeled design, and was asked to produce a pilot model. A mock-up, under the designation T 18, was produced in December 1941. However, during the design work it had been decided, at a meeting between the British and US Tank Committees, that the 37mm gun was not powerful enough and was to be replaced with the British 6 pdr (57mm). The pilot model was modified and redesignated T 18E2. The new turret was from the T 7E2 light tank and the mounting was supplied by the Rock Island Arsenal in May 1942.

When completed, the T 18E2 was considerably heavier than the proposed all up weight of 32,000 lb, at 53,000 lb. After trials in which it came in for heavy criticism, it was decided, that as none of the military representatives at the trials showed any interest, the project should be cancelled. However, the British had placed an order for 2,500 in February 1942, which was increased to 2,800 in March, but by the time production was ready to start, the North African Campaign was nearing its end and so only thirty production models were completed and sent to the United Kingdom. They named it the 'Boarhound'. They arrived in the United Kingdom in 1943, but were never used operationally, although they saw service as training vehicles. The Tank Museum's 'Boarhound' came from the School of Tank Technology and is the only remaining 'Boarhound' in existence.

The Tank Museum's T18E2 'Boarhound' is the only one still left in existence of the 30 built by the USA for the British Army.

Boarhound at the US Aberdeen
Proving Ground for trials in 1942.

SPECIFICATIONS

Manufacturer:	Yellow Truck and Coach Co. (Division of General Motors).
Pattern Date:	1943
Condition:	non-runner
Engine:	Twin General Motors 6-cylinder, in-line water-cooled, 127 bhp at 3000 rpm
Max. Speed:	50 mph
Range:	300 miles
Armour:	9 - 50 mm
Armament:	6 pounder (57 mm) and 2 x 7.62 mm Browning machine-guns
Crew:	5
Length:	20'6"
Height:	2.62 m
Width:	10'1"
Weight:	26.8 tons

Char B1-Bis
30002

The development of the Renault Char de Bataille B1 Bis began in the 1920s when, at the request of General Estienne ('Father of the French Tank Corps') and on the basis of studies by Renault, FAMH, FMC and Schneider, a new battle tank was developed under the code name 'Tracteur 30'. The specifications called for a vehicle with high mobility and heavy fire power. The result was the appearance, in 1929-30, of three pilot models built by Renault and FMC and designated Char B (B1). Production began in April 1935 and thirty-five of this model, the Char B1, were produced.

The B1-bis evolved from the Char B1, the production version of the Char B and was the main French heavy battle tank in 1940. Early production models were powered by a 250 hp engine but were later re-engined with a 300 hp Renault aircraft engine, giving a top speed of 18 mph and a range of 87 miles.

The B1 had a short 75mm carried in a front hull mounting. Sighting of the weapon was controlled by the driver, and corrections were made by moving the tank. The sophisticated Naeder Steering Unit, which allowed delicate and very accurate adjustment, had a double differential and hydrostatic drive, which gave the 'infinitely variable steering' necessary to lay the 75mm gun. This consisted of thirty-two small pistons in a brass housing, weighing almost half a ton, and gave such a degree of control that when full right lock was applied, the track on the left would rotate forwards whilst the right would reverse, allowing the vehicle to turn almost on its own axis. There was also a fixed 7.5mm machine-gun controlled by the driver, both weapons being loaded by a crewman sitting beside the driver. In the turret there was a co-axially mounted 47mm anti-tank gun and 7.5mm machine-gun, fired by the commander. This gun layout effectively halved the amount of ammunition the vehicle could carry.

Of the 365 Char B-1 bis built, large numbers were captured in a serviceable condition by the Germans in France in 1940. Although one of the most formidably armed and armoured tanks of its day, the captured B1s were not immediately issued to German fighting units, because of the limitations of the one-man turret and the tank's general performance, but instead were used as training vehicles. From 1942 they were fitted with a German radio set and used to equip German second line armour units, mainly in the West. They were also used for occupation duties in Guernsey and Jersey, serving under the German nomenclature PzKpfw Renault B-2

Our Char B1 Bis still marked STT (School of Tank Technology).

This captured Char B1 Bis was fitted by the Germans with a flamethrower in place of its normal main armament. It was known as 'Flammwagen auf Panzerkampfwagen B-2(f)'.

740(f). Some did see combat both in Russia, with the 223rd Panzerkompanie who had four B1-bis, and in the Balkans with the SS-Division *Prinz Eugen* who had seven.

The vehicle in the Museum is tank No 114 which served with Panzer Abteilung 213, First Company, 1st Platoon, as No 4 Tank. Panzer Abteilung 213 was specifically formed, in the autumn of 1941, to operate French tanks. They arrived in Jersey and Guernsey in March and April 1942 on the SS *Derindje* and SS *Livadia*. The regiment had seventeen B1-bis on Jersey and nineteen on Guernsey. Five of the vehicles on each island had been modified by the Germans, who removed the 75mm hull gun and replaced it with a flame-thrower; these vehicles were re-designated the PzKpfw B1 bis mit Flammenwerfer. Panzer Abteilung 213 was the only armoured regiment which served throughout the war on British territory and yet never fired a shot in anger.

After the Normandy landings of 6th June 1944, it was only a matter of time until control of the French coast was in the hands of the Allies, and when, on 15th August, the French port of St Malo surrendered, the door was closed on the last source of supplies for the German troops occupying the Channel Islands. The winter of 1944 was a harsh and bitter one, made worse for both Islanders and Occupiers by the virtual state of siege under which they found themselves. The British Liberation Task Force 135 arrived on 9th May, 1945, and the Islands were retaken without bloodshed. The tank crews were sent to PoW camps on the English mainland and the vehicles assembled and in May 1946, the B1s were returned to France, except for No 114 which was sent to the School of Tank Technology in the UK and subsequently was donated by them to the Tank Museum.

SPECIFICATIONS

Manufacturer:	Renault, Billancourt Seine, France.
Pattern Date:	1937
Condition:	non-runner
Engine:	Renault petrol-fuelled, 6-cylinder, liquid-cooled, 307 bhp.
Max. Speed:	28km/h
Range:	150 kms
Armour:	60mm max.
Armament:	1 75 mm gun and 1 7.5mm machine-gun fixed, low front hull.
	1 47 mm gun and co-axial 7.5mm machine-gun in turret
Crew:	4
Length:	6.38 m (20'11")
Height:	2.80 m (9'2")
Width:	2.50 m (8'2")
Weight:	32 tons

Infantry Tank, Churchill Mk VII
T 347848M

In September 1939, the General Staff, with the spectre of World War One's trench warfare in mind, produced outline specifications for a new Heavy Infantry Tank, the A 20. It was to be immune to artillery fire and able to cross heavily shelled areas of no-mans land in support of the infantry (for A20 specifications *see* TOG II*).

The first pilot model A 20E1 was ready on 11th June 1940, although it was made in mild steel and was without turret and armament. It was 27 feet 1½ inches in length, 9 feet 9½ inches in height, 9 feet 2½ inches in width and was later fitted with a Matilda (A 12) turret complete with 2 pdr main gun. Unfortunately, the A 20E1 was overweight at 43 tons (the original specification was for 32 tons, which was later changed, during the design stage to 37½ tons) and underpowered. On its first run the gearbox seized after only four miles.

In June 1940, after just two of the pilot models (A 20E1 aand A 20E2) had been completed, the project was deemed unsatisfactory and terminated. The Department of Tank Design then produced new specifications under the designation A22 and asked Vauxhall Motors to produce a design using their newly developed 350hp Twin-Six engine.

Under pressure from the Prime Minister, Winston Churchill, to produce five to six hundred tanks by Spring 1941, the revised specifications were approved and the production of the vehicle given top priority. By November 1940 design work was nearing completion and a mock-up of the 'A22 Infantry Tank Mk IV' was viewed by the Tank Design Board. By December, the first pilot model had been completed and was undergoing trials and by March 1941 the first production model had been produced in mild steel. In June, the A 22 was named the 'Churchill', much to the delight of the Prime Minister who had continued to take an active interest in the project. The first completed production models were delivered to the Army on 30th June 1941.

The Churchill first saw action during the Dieppe raid in August 1942, and there were many problems. The landings were heavily opposed and the vehicles which did make it ashore found the going impossible on the steep shingle beach. A handful

Churchill Mk II; note the Besa machine-gun which replaced the 3-inch howitzer in the hull on the Churchill Mk I.

A proud Winston Churchill inspects his namesake tanks during an exercise in 1942.

of Mark IIIs played a minor part in the Battle of Alamein in October 1943 and proved themselves almost immune to anti-tank gun fire.

The final production version was the A22F. It was the first British tank of this size to employ welded, rather than riveted, construction techniques. It also featured a new turret, which was a composite of cast plate and welds, and round crew access doors, instead of square, to reduce the stress in the armour plates in which they were set. It was produced in two versions; the Mark VII mounting a 75mm gun and, produced concurrently, the Mark VIII mounting a 95mm Howitzer. Later versions, the Marks IX, X, XI, were all rebuilds, to Mark VII standards, of earlier models. Many 'Funnies' were also developed from the Marks VII and VIII, including AVREs (Armoured Vehicle Royal Engineers), Bridgelayers, ARKs and Crocodiles (flamethrower versions).

The Mark VII saw action from D-Day onwards and ultimately in Korea. Thereafter, they were slowly phased out in favour of the Centurion.

The Museum's model was the last off the production line at Vauxhall's Luton factory. A plaque on the front of the turret, commemorates this event.

SPECIFICATIONS

Manufacturer:	Vauxhall Motors Ltd, Luton, Beds.
Pattern Date:	1945.
Condition:	runner
Engine:	Bedford Twin-Six, 12-cylinder horizontally-opposed. 350 bhp at 2,200 rpm
Max. Speed:	13 mph
Range:	127 miles
Armour:	25 - 152mm
Armament:	75mm QFSA gun.
Co-axial:	7.92mm BESA machine-gun
Front Hull:	7.92mm BESA machine-gun
Crew:	5
Length:	24'2"
Height:	8'10"
Width:	10'10"
Weight:	41 tons

Goliath (Sd Kfz 303)

Goliath, known by the Germans as Leichter Ladunstrager, came in two versions. The first, was the Sd Kfz 302 (E-Motor), which was designed to carry an explosive charge. It was a development of the Borgward BI and BII Minenräumwagen Sd Kfz 300, which had been designed as remote control minefield-clearance vehicles. The initial SdKfz 302 prototype had four large wheels, and tracks based on the BII design. However, the production model had smaller wheels, which made space for side sponsons on either side, so that extra batteries could be carried to power the 2.5 kW electric engines. The second, the Sd Kfz 303 (V-Motor) was an upgraded version of the Sd Kfz 302. It was bigger, had thicker armour and by using a 703cc Zündapp motorcycle engine, it was able to carry a heavier charge further. Two models of the SD Kfz 303 were built. The initial version was smaller and lighter:

	Length	Width	Height	Weight
Sd Kfz 303a	1.62m	0.84m	0.60m	0.37 tons
Sd Kfz 303b	1.63m	0.91m	0.62m	0.43 tons

It also carried only 75 kilos of explosives; the heavier version carried 100 kg Sprengladung.

The device was intended to be used against pill-boxes and other strong points or to blast a path through a mine-field. For normal transport to the scene of the action, the vehicle was carried on a two-wheel trailer from which it would be dismounted and be sent by wire guidance the final distance (a maximum of 650 metres) to the target. Two wires were needed to guide the vehicle and one to detonate the explosive.

All in all, approximately seven thousand Goliaths were produced. The first to be issued went to the Panzerpionier Kompanien 811-815, part of the HeerespionierBataillon (MOT) ZbV 600 (Taifun).

The Goliath was one of a number of exhibits donated to the Museum in 1951 by the Ministry of Supply. Since it has been at the Museum it has been used in many different public, and publicity, events, thanks to its small weight and size, which makes it one of the few Museum exhibits to be easily transported. In 1983, it was used as a collection box, at the entrance to the Tank Museum, and raised over £4,000 towards the costs of modernisation.

'Goliath', the smallest tank in the Museum is a Leichter Ladunstrager – a remotely controlled tracked demolition charge. This is the 1942 version, the Sd Kfz 303 (V Motor).

Preparing a 'Goliath' for action on the Eastern Front.

SPECIFICATIONS

Manufacturer:	Zündapp, Nurnberg, Germany.
Pattern Date:	1943
Condition:	non-runner
Engine:	Zündapp 527, 2-cylinder, 703 cc, 12.5 ps at 4500 rpm.
Max. Speed:	12 kmph
Range:	12kms*
Armour:	10 mm mild steel
Armament:	None. Dependent on model an explosive charge of up to 100 kg could be carried
Crew:	none
Length:	1.63 m
Height:	0.62 m
Width:	0.91 m
Weight:	0.43 tons

*Approx 650m of guidance wire carried internally on a drum.

Grant M3
T 24689

In 1939, when Germany invaded Poland, the United States of America was the only major nation with practically no tanks (400 in total, of which 375 where M2 light tanks or M1 combat cars) and no facilities to produce them. The Rock Island Arsenal had been the producer of most of the US experimental and production armoured vehicles between the wars, but it was primarily an artillery production plant. However, contingency plans had been made for heavy engineering firms to produce tanks in quantity, should there ever be a need.

On 10th July 1940, General Adna R. Chaffee was placed in charge of the newly formed Armored Force, with the responsibility for tank design and production. In August he arranged a meeting with the Ordnance Department at the Aberdeen Proving Ground to plan future tank requirements. It was proposed that a new medium tank should be built, with heavier armour and mounting a 75mm main gun in the turret. Unfortunately, mounting a weapon of such size in a turret was not feasible at the time and a new turret had to be developed. It was decided that, while development work was continuing into the problems of the turret, the need for a 75mm gun could be met by mounting the weapon in the front hull.

The M2A1 medium tank chassis was to be used, almost complete, including engine, suspension (vertical volute) and most other mechanical parts – only the hull and superstructure needed to be changed, and these were to be based on the T5E2. The turret, armed with a 37mm gun, was to be retained but offset to the left on the hull top. Both 75mm and 37mm guns were fitted with revolutionary gyrostabilizers, which would maintain the guns at any desired elevation while the tank pitched and rolled as it moved over rugged country. Up to this time, tanks could only fire accurately while stationary, so the advent of the gyrostabilizer gave the Grant the considerable tactical advantage of being able to fire accurately on the move.

In early December 1940, while the design work was proceeding on the M3 at the Aberdeen Proving Ground, building work started on a 100-acre site just outside Detroit for the planned Detroit Arsenal. At the same time, as the M3 drawings were completed, Chrysler were designing the 'plant' for the Arsenal. Design work also began, at the Watervliet Arsenal, on the 75mm gun – which was to be based on the famous French 75mm Field Gun.

The medium M3 Grant tank seen here on the range in the Middle East has some VIP spectators on its back decks, viz: C in C Middle East Gen Sir Claude Auchinleck (in forage cap), GOC 7th Armd Div Maj Gen 'Jock' Campbell VC (in centre) and Brig Alec Gatehouse (seated).

A Grant in Libya, in 1942, camouflaged to give the appearance of a lorry.

Final design work was completed in March 1941 and the pilot models were finished by April. It was decided that as well as the 1,000 vehicles ordered from the Detroit Arsenal, orders would be placed with the American Locomotive Co, (685 M3 tanks) and the Baldwin Locomotive Works (534 M3 tanks).

The M3 was widely used by the British, who had only 150 effective tanks remaining after the withdrawal from Dunkirk. Large numbers were ordered from the Baldwin and Lima Locomotive Works but modified to suit British requirements. The main change was to the turret, which by British standards was too high. This was lowered and fitted with British radio equipment and the machine-gun cupola, seen in the US design, was eliminated. The first British version was completed in November 1940 and deliveries were rushed to North Africa in 1942.

The Grant, named after the famous American Civil War hero General Ulysses Grant, first saw action in the Battle of Gazala and proved a considerable shock to the Germans. On 26th May 1942, 15 miles east of Bir Hacheim, Rommel had launched his Operation VENEZIA. His Italians allies attacked the Free French whilst the German 15th and 21st Panzer Divisions moved towards the British lines. Armed with Stuarts and Grants 3 RTR moved to intercept them. With the Stuarts of A Squadron protecting their flank, the nineteen Grants of B Squadron formed into a battle line along a small ridge; as the Panzer III and IVs came within 1,000 yards range, the Grants opened fire with devastating effect.

For the first time, the British had a vehicle with an accurate, high velocity gun of sufficient calibre to engage the German Panzers from beyond the effective range of their 5cm (Panzer III) and the short barreled 7.5cm guns Panzer IV).

The Museum exhibit was used as a training vehicle and was generously donated to the Museum by the Royal Armoured Corps in 1949. It is painted with the distinctive camouflage used during the North African campaign and shows the insignia of the Scots Greys.

SPECIFICATIONS

Manufacturer:	Baldwin and Pullman, Chrysler, American Locomotive Co.
Pattern Date:	1942
Condition:	non-runner
Engine:	Wright Continental R-975-EC2, 9-cylinder radial, petrol-fueled, air-cooled, 340 bhp at 2,400 rpm.
Max. Speed:	21 mph
Range:	120 miles
Armour:	½" - 2"
Armament:	Sponson; 75 mm QFSA gun. Turret; 37 mm QFSA gun. 4 x .30-inch Browning
Crew:	6
Length:	18'6"
Height:	9'11"
Width:	8'11"
Weight:	27.6 tons

Light Tank Type 95 Ha-Go
663

Developed in 1933, at the Sagami Army Arsenal, to bring mobility to their newly created experimental armoured brigades, the Ha-Go (sometimes called Ke-Go, or Kyu-Go), Light Tank Type 95 was the most outstanding and effective Japanese tank of World War Two.

Specifications called for a vehicle of around 7 tons, with a speed of 25 mph, a 37mm main gun in a fully traversing turret and a machine-gun in the hull next to the driver. The first prototype was completed in June 1934 and a year later a second was commenced which was finished in November 1935. This was standardised as the Light Tank Type 95. Its hull and turret were constructed from rolled steel plates which were mainly riveted or bolted in position, although welding was used in some places. The turret was offset to the left of the hull and the front machine-gun was in a built-out compartment.

It was tested in Manchuria and was popular due to its reliability. The air-cooled diesel engine was of a very advanced design and had a high power to weight ratio. Its reliability and sustainable high speed ensured that it played an essential role in Japanese victories in China, Malaysia, Phillipines and the Pacific Islands. But the Japanese field commanders seldom used their armour in the role laid down in their Field Service Regulations (much of which were based on the writings of Fuller, Liddell-Hart and Guderian) but used them in the infantry support role. Much of the Japanese success in the early part of the war was as a result of the low standard of equipment of the opposition and, to a large extent, the eastern jungle and island terrain – which was totally unsuitable for armoured combat but ideal for the Japanese

A knocked-out Type 95 light tank 'Ha-Go' after an ambush. The bodies of the crew can be seen in the background.

A knocked-out Ha-Go, dwarfed by an American LVT (Landing Vehicle Tracked), in the Pacific Islands.

infantry role. The Ha-Go gun, having a minimum depression of only 20 degrees, left a 23-foot blind area all around itself, which could not be covered by the armament, so it was extremely vulnerable to ambush, on the jungle tracks.

Production was discontinued in 1943 but the Ha-Go remained in service until the end of the war and formed the basis for several new designs, such as:

Type 98 Ke-Ni Light Tank: heavier armour and armament (47mm high velocity gun) and better performance engine uprated to 140 hp, speed increased to 30 mph).

Type 4 Ke-Nu: turret of a type 97 Medium Chi-Ha (57mm maingun) on the type 95 hull

Type 2 Ka-Mi: amphibious Type 95 Light, with new hull and detachable pontoons to provide the amphibious capability.

The Museum's Ha-Go was donated by the Ministry of Supply in 1951.

SPECIFICATIONS

Manufacturer:	Mitsubishi Jukogyo K.K., Japan
Pattern Date:	1936
Condition:	non-runner
Engine:	Mitsubishi 6-cylinder overhead valve, air-cooled, diesel-fueled, 120 bhp at 1,800 rpm.
Max. Speed:	28 mph
Range:	120 miles
Armour:	6 - 12 mm
Armament:	37 mm tank gun. 2 x 7.7 mm machine guns
Crew:	3 (commander/gunner, driver, hull gunner)
Length:	14'4½"
Height:	7'2"
Width:	6'9"
Weight:	7.4 tons

Hanomag
SdKfz 251/1

The first Armoured Infantry Carrying Vehicle was the Armstrong Whitworth Mk IX, which appeared in 1918, and was designed to carry either thirty infantrymen or 10 tons of supplies. Unfortunately, after 1918 the general military opinion in Great Britain and France was that the future role of the armoured vehicle, specifically the tank, was as an infantry support vehicle. However, the forward thinking Captain Basil Liddell Hart had already envisaged the potential of an 'integrated', mobile armoured force. In Germany, also, the idea of an armoured force backed by mobile infantry, artillery, engineers and service support was already being developed.

By 1933, armoured forces in divisional strength had been planned and created, and were already in training. However, as the frontline panzer divisions had top priority, the infantry used ordinary commercial wheeled transport. It was soon realised by the German High Command that units equipped purely with wheeled vehicles would never achieve the mobility necessary, especially in rough terrain, to keep up with their fully-tracked counterparts. Although for long distance movement by road, wheels obviously had the advantage.

The solution was already in existence in Germany, where by 1927-28 excellent half-track military vehicles were already being manufactured, mostly for use as towing tractors, and where by 1935 plans were made to provide armour for these vehicles. The best of these, ideal for carrying a fully-equipped Infantry Squad, was the 3 ton half-track tractor developed by Hansa-Lloyd-Goliath Werke AG (later Borgward). A development period followed, between 1934 and 1938, in which various prototypes were tested and various minor modifications made. By the end of 1938 the Gepanzerter Mannschafts Transportwagen (MTW) prototype APC 'H 8 (H)' and 'H k1 6' had been completed.

The standard vehicle was Ackerman-steered by the wheeled front axle, linked to track brakes activated by the steering wheel, with the engine and major weight of the vehicle being supported by light weight, highly sophisticated, lubricated tracks, supported on eight pairs of road wheels. It had armour between 8 and 14.5 mm thick and was powered by a Mayback HL 42 TUKRM six-cylinder, water-cooled, petrol engine, manufactured by Mordbau and Auto-Union. The body was a rigid,

A line of Hanomags move into action in Russia.

A Hanomag carrying a full Infantry Section.

welded frame, which was further strengthened by the underbelly and hull armour plating (which in Ausführungen A to C was both welded and bolted). The ballistically-shaped hull was open at the top, but could be covered by a canvas cover in adverse weather conditions.

The H 8 (H) version could carry a nine-man squad, commander and driver. The Ordnance number for this family of vehicles was Sonderkraftfahrzeug 251, and the official designation Mittlerer Gepanzerter Mannschaftskraftwagen, Hanomag Company of Hannover was given the task of producing the chassis and Buessing-NAG of Berlin-Oberschoeneweide the production of the armoured superstructure.

In late 1938, final trials of the Hanomag were held at Kummersdorf and the first units, a company of the 1st Panzer Division (stationed in Weimar), were equipped in the spring of 1939. They first saw action in the German invasion of Poland and the Germans learned many practical lessons in their use and potential use, as can be seen in the number and types of variants.

In 1940, the Ausf A and B were superseded by the Ausf C which continued in production up to late 1943. A fourth model, the Ausf D which had a smaller number of separate armour plates, was then introduced with the aim of simplifying production so that more could be produced. In all no fewer than 15,252 SdKfz 251 were produced and they were used for a wide variety of tasks.

There were twenty-five main variants. SdKfz 251/1 – standard armoured personnel carrier (three different loads – a panzergrenadier section, a heavy machine-gun group or 6 x Wurfrahmen 40 as a heavy bombardment vehicle), 251/2 – 8cm mortar carrier, (251/3) – wireless, command vehicle, (251/4) – ammunition carrier which towed the light 75mm infantry howitzer, – (251/5) – engineer wireless vehicle (two types), (251/6) – command post, (251/7) – engineer equipment carrier (eg: small assault bridges, mines, etc), (251/8) – armoured ambulance, (251/9) – 7.5 cm KwK37 (L/24) tank gun carrier, (251/10) – 3.7cm PaK 35/36 (L/45) gun carrier, (251/11) – telephone exchange and cable-laying vehicle, (251/12) – artillery survey section vehicle, (251/13) – artillery sound recording vehicle, (251/14) – artillery sound ranging vehicle, (251/15) – artillery flash spotting vehicle, (251/16) – flamethrower (2 x 1.4cm flammenwerfer), (251/17) – AA vehicle mounting 2cm Flak 38, (251/18) – artillery observation post vehicle, (251/19) – mobile telephone exchange vehicle, (251/20) – searchlight vehicle (to support Panther units equipped with I-R sights, (251/21) – AA vehicle equipped with triple mounted AA 1.5 cm heavy machine-cannons (ex-fighter aircraft), (251/22) – AA vehicle mounting a 7.5cm PAK 40 L/46, 251/23 – semi-tracked armoured car, mounting 2cm KwK38, 251 Munitionspanzer – ammunition transport, 251 7.5cm PaK 42/L70 – experimental only.

As can be seen, therefore, it proved to be an all-round tool, useful in both tactical and strategic roles, for both attack and defence, reconnaissance and communication, as well as for the roles for which it was designed – the mass and swift movement of men and *materiél*. It allowed the German Army to patent its tactic of *Blitzkrieg*, giving the necessary mobility to the infantry and support units in the extended lines of communication, without which this type of warfare would prove impossible.

Armoured ambulance, Sd Kfz 251/8 mittlerer Krankenpanzerwagen.

The vehicle in the Museum is the SdKfz 251/8, Ausf C Kranken Panzerwagen, which served as an armoured ambulance with a crew of two. They could cope with either four stretcher cases or ten lightly injured cases, or a combination of both. It was the 44th Hanomag to be built by BMM. It was captured in North Africa and kindly donated to the Museum in 1951 by the Ministry of Supply. One particularly 'sensitive' visitor to the Museum told staff that, when she was looking in the back of the Hanomag, she heard the screams and groans of dead and dying men, emanating from this vehicle.

In order to make full use of the Hanomag in the Blitzkrieg diorama, we have changed it back into a normal SdKfz 251/1 medium APC and crewed it with panzergrenadiers.

SPECIFICATIONS

Manufacturer:	Bohmisch-Marische Maschinenfabrik (BMM)
Pattern Date:	1941
Condition:	non-runner
Engine:	Maybach HL 42 TUKRM 6-cylinder in-line, petrol-fuelled, water-cooled, 100 bhp at 2,800 rpm
Max. Speed:	53 mph
Range:	120 miles
Armour:	8 - 14.5 mm
Armament:	nil as ambulance
Crew:	2 (carries 10)
Length:	5.98m
Height:	1.75m
Width:	2.1m
Weight:	8 tons

Jagdpanther (SdKfz 173)
PANZERJÄGER FÜR 8.8CM PAK 43 AUF FGST PANTHER I

By late 1942, the German Army needed a fast, well-armed, tank-destroyer able to knock out the Allies' heaviest tanks. The choice of weapon was the formidable 8.8 cm PaK 43/3 L/71 anti-aircraft gun, already renowned for its devastating effect as an anti-tank gun. The chassis selected for the vehicle was the new Panther Ausf A, with a ball-mounted machine-gun in the glacis.

Maschinenfabrik Neidersachsen-Hannover (MNH) developed the prototype which was demonstrated to Hitler on 20th October 1943, at Arys. He gave his approval and full production began at the Brunswick factory of Muhlenbau und Industrie AG (MIAG), in January 1944, and at MNH by the end of the year. Production of the Jagdpanther continued at both factories until March 1945, by which time total production figures show that 392 had been built.

The turretless superstructure was formed by extending the upper hull and side plates of the normal Panther chassis, to provide a roomy, flat topped fighting compartment to mount the 8.8cm PaK. The armour was thick (frontal armour 80mm) and well sloped to deflect incoming shells. As with Hetzer, the main gun had limited elevation (-8 degrees to +14 degrees) and traverse (13 degrees left to 13 degrees right), so the gun had to be laid by movement of the vehicle.

It was a fearsome and intimidating tank destroyer in both defence and attack, and the power of its gun – the recommended engagement range for the 8.8cm PaK was 2,469 m (2,700 yds) – was enhanced by its cross country mobility. An even more powerful variant was being investigated by Krupp, who drew up a design (Hln-E 143) dated 17th November 1944 for a Jagdpanther armed with a 12.8cm PaK 80 L/55; but this was never built.

The Museum's Jagdpanther was found partly completed, as was the Panther, on the production lines after the German surrender. It was completed, in Hanover, by German workmen under the supervision of REME technicians from 823 Armoured Workshop, REME. It was one of an unlikely troop of three Panthers and seven Jagdpanthers which arrived at the Driving and Maintenance Wing, Bovington Camp

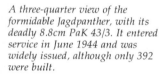

A three-quarter view of the formidable Jagdpanther, with its deadly 8.8cm PaK 43/3. It entered service in June 1944 and was widely issued, although only 392 were built.

in 1946, for 'Investigation and Demonstration' purposes. Of the ten vehicles, the Museum's Jagdpanther and Panther are, as far as is known, the only ones remaining, apart from one Panther now at the Panzer Museum in Munster Oertze. The rest were probably used as 'hard targets' on the ranges at Lulworth. It remains potentially a good runner, but has not been tested for many years.

Side view of the same vehicle.

SPECIFICATIONS

Manufacturer:	Maschinenfabrik Neidersachsen-Hannover
Pattern Date:	1944
Condition:	runner
Engine:	Maybach HL 230 P 30 V12, petrol-fueled, water-cooled, 700 bhp at 3,000 rpm
Max. Speed:	46 km/ph
Range:	160 km
Armour:	25 - 80mm
Armament:	8.8cm PaK 43/3 L/71. 7.92mm MG 34
Crew:	5
Length:	9.90 m
Height:	2.72 m
Width:	3.42 m
Weight:	46 tons

Jagdpanzer 38(t) Hetzer (Baiter)
(PANZERJGER 38(T)) FR 7.5CM PAK 39)
3222111

Colonel General Heinz Guderian, the talented German field commander and 'father' of the Panzerwaffe, was made Inspector-General of Armoured Troops on 1st March 1943. With his vast experience of tank warfare he was the perfect man for the job and had strong opinions on what type of vehicles were needed. One of his first demands was for a low silhouette, light tank destroyer, with good armour protection, to replace the light self-propelled guns and towed anti-tank guns.

It was to be developed from the chassis of the PzKpfw 38(t) which was the German designation given to the Czech Lt vz 38, produced by Bohmisch-Marische Maschinenfabrik (formerly CKD) for the Wehrmacht, after the annexation of the Czechoslovakian provinces of Bohemia and Moravia in March 1939. After winning a competition in 1938, an order had been placed for 150 LT vz 38s but, due to the Munich agreement, they were still incomplete by the time of the German occupation. After the occupation, the Wehrmacht quickly placed an order for the completion of these vehicles and they were first used operationally in the assault on Poland.

Tests were completed in December 1943 and the production line at the BMM plant, still producing the PzKpfw 38 (t) and variants, was switched quickly to production of the Panzerjäger, which began in April 1944. Later in the same year, Skoda and Krupp also participated in the production programme.

'Hetzer' became one of the most advanced anti-tank vehicles of the war with total production figures of 2,584 between April 1944 and May 1945. It was a radical design, although using many components of the Pz Kpfw 38 (t), with a low profile, wide hull and well angled armour. Although the fighting compartment proved a little

An American GI leans nonchalantly on a knocked-out Hetzer Jagdpanzer 38(t).

cramped in battle and the limited angle of fire also presented problems, with its powerful 7.5cm PaK 39 L/48 and 60mm frontal armour it proved an excellent tank hunter/killer.

A rear overhead view of an early production model of Hetzer.

Panzerjägerabteilungen 731 and 743 were the first combat units to receive Hetzer in July 1944, and the 15th and 76th were the first Infantry Divisions to have its anti-tank battallions equipped with it.

The Museum's Hetzer was donated by the Ministry of Supply in 1951.

SPECIFICATIONS

Manufacturer:	BMM (Bohmisch-Marische Maschinenfabrik) formerly CKD), Prague, Czechoslovakia.
Pattern Date:	November/December 1944
Condition:	non-runner
Engine:	Czech EPA, overhead valve, 6-cylinder, water-cooled, petrol-fueled, 150 bhp.
Max. Speed:	42 km/ph
Range:	177 km
Armour:	8 - 60 mm
Armament:	7.5 cm PaK 39 L/48. 1 x 7.92 mm MG 34 or 42
Crew:	4
Length:	6.38 m
Height:	2.17 m
Width:	2.63 m
Weight:	15.75 tons

Klementi Voroshilov KV 1B

Design of a new tank had started in the Soviet Union in 1938. A new 76 mm tank gun had been manufactured, which could fire both HE and AP rounds, and a new V12 engine had sucessfully passed through extensive trials. The new vehicle was to be developed from the multi-turreted SMK (Sergius Mironovitch Kirov).

Under the watchful eyes of Stalin himself, a group of engineers at Kirov headed by I. T. Kotin decided that the heavy tank, which was practically invulnerable to 37mm anti tank weapons, should have only one turret with one very powerful gun. Kotin took his design to the Kremlin where it was approved by Stalin and named the KV, after Marshal of the Soviet Union Klimenti Voroshilov.

The first models entered service in 1939 and they saw action in Finland, on the final assault on the Mannerheim Line. Although difficult to drive and with a complicated internal layout, which hampered its performance in action – the commander loaded the gun and the assistant driver operated the machine-gun in the rear of the turret – its powerful gun, almost impregnable armour and reliable engine ensured that the KV series was used throughout the war. In all, over 13,500 vehicles were built on the KV chassis including the KV 1A, KV 1B (bolted turret), KV 1B (cast turret), KV 1C, KC 1s (s – standing for *skorostnoy* or 'fast'), the KV 2 series and the Joseph Stalin heavy tanks which appeared at the end of the war.

The vehicle in the Museum is the KV1 B, which was developed in 1941 to combat the effect of German anti-tank guns at close range. Improvements from the 1A were the addition of appliqué armour: 25-35 mm to the hull front, 35 mm to the parts of the side superstructure and turret sides and bars of metal protecting the turret base (KV 1B [bolted turret]). This increased the weight from 43.5 tons to 47 tons. The gun

Front view of a KV-1B in a Soviet camp.

was also upgraded from the 76 mm, 30.5 calibre, to the M 1940 76 mm, 41.5 calibre. *A super detail shot of the KV-1B.*
During early 1942, cast turrets replaced the older version and the overhang at the base of the turret was eliminated to stop shells being deflected into the body of the vehicle; these were designated KV1B (cast turret).

KV 1s were originally built at the Kirovskiy Works, Leningrad, but following the German invasion (Operation BARBAROSSA) in June 1941 the factory was evacuated to Chelyabinsk in the Urals, soon to become the largest tank engineering combine in the USSR. Women not only built and repaired these tanks but are reputed to have fought in them, in the Soviet Army. The Russian writing on the turret reads;

"For Leningrad
From Leningrad women to the Front."

This tank was built at the new Chelyabinsk complex, popularly known as 'Tankograd', and was given to the British Army in 1943, by the Soviet Union for evaluation in 1941. It was sent to the RAC Scool of Tank Technology, Chertsey, where it remained until 1952 when they generously donated it to the Tank Museum. It has been on display ever since.

SPECIFICATIONS

Manufacturer:	Kirovskiy Works, Leningrad
	Chelyabinsk Works, Urals
Pattern Date:	1941
Condition:	non-runner
Engine:	Type V-2K 60, V-12, water-cooled, diesel-fueled, 600 bhp
Max. Speed:	21 mph (35 km/ph)
Range:	210 miles
Armour:	30 - 90 mm
Armament:	76.2 mm (M 1941 ZIS-5)
	4 x DT 7.62 mm machine-guns
Crew:	5 (Commander/gunner, driver, gunner, radio-operator/
	hull machine-gunner, mechanic/assistant driver)
Length:	22'7"
Height:	8'9"
Width:	10'8"
Weight:	47 tons

Matilda IIA
(Infantry Tank A12)
T 10459

In April 1934, outline specifications were produced for two types of 'infantry' tank;

A small machine-gun tank, mounting a .303-inch or .50-inch machine-gun, to act as mobile machine gun posts;

A heavy tank, mounting a high velocity 2 pdr A-T gun, to deal with enemy tanks and fortified machine-gun positions.

The first pilot model of the A11 'Infantry Tank Mk I', designed by Sir John Carden and produced by Vickers in 1936, was powered by a Ford V8 engine (maximum speed 8 mph – Infantry tanks required only enough speed to keep up with infantry in the attack *i.e.* walking pace) and armed with either a .303-inch or .5-inch machine-gun.

There are a number of stories as to how the tank got its nickname: 'Matilda', one being that General Sir Hugh Elles, then Master-General of Ordnance, when he saw the tank's comic, duck-like appearance, and gait, dubbed it 'Matilda', after a cartoon series of the day. However, we have still to discover anyone who can actually remember the cartoon character 'Matilda Duck' and it seems more likely that the name was coined by Sir John Carden much earlier. In fact the codeword 'Matilda' appears on the original proposal for the A11 in Carden's handwriting. 139 Mk 1s were produced and although they were cheap and reliable, they were soon out-moded. They did see action in the early days of the war but therafter were used for training purposes.

In 1936, design began on its sucessor which was to mount a 2 pdr maingun and have an increased speed of around 10-15 mph. It was hoped to modify the A11 but it soon became apparent that this would not be practical. Instead, the new design, designated the A12 'Infantry Tank Mk II', would be based on the A7 medium tank, designed and built (in prototype form only) by the Royal Ordnance Factory, Wool-wich in 1929-32.

In November 1936, the Vulcan Foundry of Warrington was given the contract to build wooden mock-ups and mild steel pilot models. These were completed by April 1937, when it was decided to install twin-ganged AEC diesel engines and a Wilson epicyclic gear box. It was armed with a co-axially mounted 2 pdr and 7.92mm Besa.

A Matilda II belonging to X troop, from 7th RTR, stationed in Malta. The stone pattern camouflage was unique to the George Cross Island. It is dragging a Bristol Beaufort torpedo bomber damaged during an attack on the Italian Fleet in late 1941.

A Matilda III receives a near miss from a German bomb, Tobruk 1941. The Mark III was the same as the Mark II but powered by a Leyland engine.

The turret could be traversed in fourteen seconds, with a powered traverse adapted from the Nash and Thompson system – fitted to the Vickers A9, the first tank to have powered traverse. The hull armour was cast and the tracks were protected by one-piece armour side skirts, with five mud chutes. In December, orders were placed for sixty-five vehicles 'off the drawing board'; this was increased to 165 in May 1938.

The Matilda played its most important role in the early Western Desert campaigns. In Libya, in 1940, its heavy armour was soon found to be almost immune to Italian anti-tank and tank fire. Until the appearance of the German 88mm Flak gun, used in an anti-tank role (June/July 1941), it was the most effective of the British AFVs.

Unfortunately, as the Matilda turret could not fit the 6 pdr, due to the small size of its turret ring, its importance began to diminish. However, many special purpose variants were produced, including the following:

Matilda CDL: Canal Defence Light, a powerful searchlight used to illuminate battlefields in night conditions. It was also meant to confuse and distract the enemy;
Baron I, II, III and IIIA: mine clearance versions;
Matilda Scorpion: mine clearance device;
Matilda with AMRA Mk Ia: mine clearance device, using Fowler rollers;
Matilda with Carrot: Carrot demolition charge (600 lb HE);
Matilda Frog: flame-throwing device;
Matilda Murray: flame-throwing device;
Matilda Dozer/Matilda with Inglis Bridge/Matilda with trench crossing device.
A total of 2,987 was completed between 1940 and 1943.

The Museum exhibit was donated to the Tank Museum in 1949 by the Royal Armoured Corps. It was a training vehicle and has always been kept in good running order. It was last used in the LWT programme *This Is Your Life*, honouring Major General Bob Foote VC, DSO, when the tank was taken onto the driving circuit at RARDE Chertsey in late 1986, during the initial presentation by Eamon Andrews, who arrived in a Chieftain, complete the RTR beret! In Gen Bob's honour the Matilda had been painted to represent his tank 'Golden Miller', in which he was commanding 7th RTR, when he was awarded the Victoria Cross for outstanding courage and leadership over the period 27th May to 15th June 1942 in the bitter 'Cauldron' battles. The unusual camouflage pattern was one of a number tried out in the Western Desert.

SPECIFICATIONS

Manufacturer:	North British Locomotive., Glasgow.
Pattern Date:	1941
Condition:	runner (1986)
Engine:	Twin AEC, 6-cylinder, diesel-fuelled, water-cooled, 87 bhp each.
Max. Speed:	15 mph
Range:	160 miles
Armour:	20 - 78 mm
Armament:	2 pdr and 7.92mm Besa machine-gun
Crew:	4
Length:	18'5"
Height:	8'
Width:	8'6"
Weight:	26.5 tons

Carro Armato M 13/40
3543

The M 13/40 was developed late in 1939 under the direction of General M. Caracciolo di Feroleto, Chief of the Superior Inspectorate of Technical Services (SITS). It was based on the M 11/39, but was bigger and carried its main armament, a new high velocity 47 mm gun and co-axial 8mm Breda machine-gun, in the turret and there were also twin 8mm Breda machine-guns, gimbal-mounted in the front hull. This was the opposite of the M 11/39 in which the 37 mm gun was in the front hull and the machine-guns in the turret.

Production of the M 13 had been delayed for some time by continuing modifications and new requirements pressed upon the designers by the Italian Tank Commission. However, with the imminent outbreak of war, under General Caracciolo di Feroleto's personal supervision SITS organised the immediate mass production of the M 13/40. Trials were held in the early part of 1940; by mid-July, fifteen production models were complete and 250 had been produced by the end of the year.

Deliveries began in the middle of 1940. They first saw action on 9th December, during the first campaign in Libya. The M13 proved a practical design with an effective main gun but there were problems – it quickly established a reputation for mechanical failure and, in the desert, it was necessary to 'Tropicalise' the vehicles, adding improved air and fuel filters. It was also underpowered and underarmoured, proving no match for the heavy British Infantry tanks like Matilda II. During General Wavell's offensive at Beda Fomm in February 1941, so many were captured (112 Medium tanks) in pristine condition, that, as an emergency measure, the 6th Royal Tank Regiment was equipped with them, as were the Australian 6th Cavalry.

M13s were also fitted with an uprated engine (Type 15T developing 125 bhp at

The Italian Carro Armato M13/40.

Knocked-out and captured M 13/40s after Beda Fomm, February 1941.

1,900 rpm as opposed to the older Type 8T producing 105 bhp at 1,800 rpm), and were then known, semi-officially, as the 'uppowered M13' or M 14/41.

Of nineteen M 13 and M 14 tanks of the Italian 3rd/XI Battalion which made a heroic charge during the Battle of Alamein on 10th July 1942, seventeen were lost. Only one tank reached its objective, number RE 3700 which also led the attack, reaching the ridge and disappearing beyond. It was later found destroyed, lying in a minefield. The vehicle was then made into a memorial and placed on the hill which was the objective of the attack, Hill 33. It remained for many years, its gun pointing towards Cairo, and may still be there to this day.

The Museum's M13/40 was donated by the Ministry of Supply in 1951.

SPECIFICATIONS

Manufacturer:	Ansaldo-Fossati – vehicle
	Fiat-SPA – engine, transmission and steering
Pattern Date:	1940
Condition:	potential runner
Engine:	SPA 90-degree V-8, water-cooled, diesel-fueled, 105 bhp
Max. Speed:	19.7 mph
Range:	124 miles
Armour:	9 - 40 mm
Armament:	47 mm QFSA and co-axial Breda 8 mm machine-gun, in turret. Twin 8 mm Breda machine-guns in front hull
Crew:	4 (Commander/gunner, driver, machine gunner, loader)
Length:	16'2"
Height:	7'9"
Width:	7'3"
Weight:	14 tons

Panther 1
PzKpfw V, Ausf G (SdKfz 171)

In October 1941, the German Panzertruppen, who had presumed their tanks to be superior to anything the enemy could produce, received a nasty shock when they first met with the Russian T 34.

Guderian, in his report to Army Group, described their marked superiority over the PzKpfw IV (the best and heaviest tank in service with the German Army at the time) and requested a team of experts to make an on-the-spot examination, in the field. The team of experts (including designers and manufacturers), arrived at the Second Panzer Army Front on 20th November 1941, examined the captured and knocked-out enemy tanks and spoke with soldiers with first-hand battle experience of the T 34. Many of the German tank crews were of the opinion that the best solution would be to take back a T 34 and simply copy and mass produce it.

The result, however, was that the Heereswaffenamt put out contracts to Daimler-Benz and MAN to build a heavy medium tank (designated the VK 3002), in the 30-35 ton class, with the following specifications;

Armour thickness	frontal arc	60mm (min.)
	sides and rear	40mm (min.)
	(Front glacis and sides to be sloped as in T-34)	
Speed:	55 km/ph (max.)	
	40 kmph (cruising)	

Allied troops inspect a captured PzKpfw V Ausf A. Note the anti-magnetic mine paste (Zimmerit) on the front glacis and mantlet.

Two very different models were produced by the competing firms; the Daimler-

A Panther knocked out by the Second French Armoured Division, under command of General Jacques Phillipe Leclerc. French civilians help to remove the tank from the house after it attempted to escape through the building.

Benz VK 3002 (DB) closely resembled the T 34, whereas MAN's VK 3002 (MAN) was more similar to other contemporary German designs. Initially, Hitler approved the Daimler-Benz design, but due to the untested MB 507 diesel engine and the fact that the desired gun would never fit into the small turret, the 'Panther Committee' approved, after minor modifications to the turret, the MAN design which was sent for trials at Kummersdorf. As a result of these sucessful trials, the new vehicle went into immediate production, with the designation PzKpfw V Panther (SdKfz 171) Ausf A (later redesignated Ausf D). Planned production was to be 250 a month initially but at the end of 1942 this target was increased to 600 a month. As MAN could clearly not cope with this demand, Daimler-Benz and later MNH and Henschel switched to Panther production.

In July 1941, Rheinmetal-Borsig had been given a contract to develop a tank gun, which could penetrate 140mm of armour at 1,000m (1,090 yds), and a turret into which it could fit. In June 1942, they began production of the long L/70, a gun which soon earned the respect and fear of every Allied tank crew.

Two Panthers could be built in the same number of man hours as one Tiger and some six thousand were built. Many considered it to be the best tank produced by any nation during World War Two. Due to the rush in which it had been developed, it did not perform well when it was first used in a major battle – of the 200 Panthers that took part, 160 were out of action by the end of the day. During the same battle, however, a T-34 was knocked out by a first round hit from a range of 7,224 m!

The final production model was the G which incorporated many design changes, some from the advice of serving tank crews. The hull had been redesigned with a greater slope and thicker armour on the sides, 50mm rather than 40mm. The front glacis was strengthened by replacing the driver's vision port with a rotating periscope, on his compartment roof. The hatches for the driver and hull gunner were improved and various minor changes made to the drive chain, to increase reliability. It was built in larger numbers than the other models, 3,740 being produced between March 1944 and April 1945.

The Ausf G saw action in France, Russia and later in East Prussia, Hungary and Belgium. Large numbers of Panthers, of all types, were used in the Ardennes offensive, including some disguised as the American M10 tank destroyer, complete with US regimental vehicle markings and US uniforms for their crews.

The Ausf G in the Museum, as with the Jagdpanther, was found partly completed on the German production lines after the German surrender and completed under the supervision of personnel from 823 Armoured Workshop, REME. Unfortunately, just the two specimens in the Museum remain; the others were probably used as hard targets on the ranges at Lulworth. Although currently a non-runner, it is potentially, like the Jagdpanther, a very good runner.

SPECIFICATIONS

Manufacturer:	Maschinenfabrik Neidersachsen-Hannover (MNH)
	MAN
	Daimler-Benz
Pattern Date:	1945
Condition:	potential runner
Engine:	Maybach HL 230 P 30, V12, petrol-fueled, water-cooled
	700 bhp at 3,000 rpm
Max. Speed:	46 km/ph
Range:	200 km
Armour:	16 110 mm
Armament:	7,5cm KwK 42 L/70.
	2 x 7.92mm MG 34
Crew:	5
Length:	8.86 m
Height:	2.98 m
Width:	3.4 m
Weight:	45.5 tons

Kleiner Panzerbefehlswagen
(Sd Kfz 265)

The Kleiner Panzerbefehlswagen (K1 Pz Bef Wg) was developed specifically for use as as an amoured command vehicle (ACV). Several were produced by modifying the Pz Kpfw I Ausf A, but the production vehicle was based on the Pz Kpfw Ausf B, which had a lengthened chassis. The purpose of the ACV was to enable the unit commander to be at the 'sharp end' with sufficient armoured protection, yet having the additional space he required for his radios, maps, etc.

Rather than a traversing turret the K1 Pz Bef Wg had a built-up fixed superstructure to provide room for the FuG6 ultra short wave receiver and 20 Watt transmitter (range six-miles) needed for an ACV. It was armed with a single ball-mounted MG 34. Approximately two hundred were built between 1935-37 and were issued to Panzer unit headquarters, from company to brigade level.

The vehicle in the Museum served with the 5th Panzer Regiment, part of the Leichte (Light) Division, arriving in Tripoli, Libya, on 10th March 1941. The 5th Panzer Regiment took part on the advance on Agedabia and Mechili and the siege

A Kleiner Befelswagen on manoeuvres. The light armoured tracked command vehicle was based upon the Pzkpfw I, with the turret modified to accommodate a radio transmitter and its operator.

of Tobruk. After its capture it was the subject of a detailed report by the School of Tank Technology, completed in 1943 after trials at Farnborough. It is the only known commanders model with extra armour bolted on the hull and superstructure. Several shot holes can be seen in the superstructure and hull.

It was donated to the Museum by the Ministry of Supply in 1951.

Befehlswagen on parade, in the background Hitler and Mussolini take the salute.

SPECIFICATIONS

Manufacturer:	Daimler-Benz,Berlin. (superstructure)
	Henschel, Kassel. (chassis)
Pattern Date:	1937
Condition:	non-runner
Engine:	Maybach NL 38 TR, 6-cylinder, petrol-fueled, water-cooled, 95 bhp
Max. Speed:	40 km/ph
Range:	170 km
Armour:	6 - 13 mm
Armament:	7.92 mm MG 34
Crew:	3
Length:	4.42 m
Height:	1.99 m
Width:	2.06 m
Weight:	5.9 tons

RAM Kangaroo

In 1940, the Canadian Defence Department had an immediate requirement for tanks but the chances of receiving any from Britain were remote, whilst all spare tank production capacity in the United States had already been ordered by the United Kingdom. The answer was to manufacture the American M3 medium tank, then in the design stage at the US Ordnance Department, in Canada at a specially constructed Tank Arsenal. Furthermore, the British and Canadians decided that they could improve upon the US M3 design by including ideas and features of their own.

The first RAM 1s, with 2 pdr main guns, were completed in the Montreal Locomotive Works in November 1941, and in January 1942 production changed to the upgunned RAM 2s, which mounted a gyro-stabilized 6 pdr as main armament. Neither version of the Ram gun tank was ever used in action, however, various variants were created for specific roles, the most important and best remembered of which was the RAM 'Kangaroo'.

During Operation TOTALISE, part of the Falaise offensive in early August 1944, Lt General Guy Simonds, Commander of the Canadian Corps, needing to transport his infantry over a large expanse of open ground, ordered the 105mm howitzers removed from Priest Self-Propelled guns (which had just been replaced by the Sexton) so that troops could be transported in them. These Priest Kangaroos or 'Unfrocked Priests' as they were popularly known, had the gun embrasure plated in and could carry twelve men.

The idea was later taken up by 79th Armoured Division, and by September 1944 the 1st Canadian Armoured Carrier Regiment was formed using converted RAM 2 tanks. The turret was removed, rungs welded to the side of the vehicle to make entry easier. The turret space provided ample room for eleven infantrymen.

Despite the major failing, namely the lack of an armoured top, RAM Kangaroos were used with such great success by the Canadians in the taking of Boulogne that,

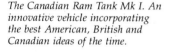

The Canadian Ram Tank Mk I. An innovative vehicle incorporating the best American, British and Canadian ideas of the time.

within a month, the British 49th Royal Tank Regiment was equipped with 120 converted RAMs and redesignated as the 49th APC Regiment.

The Canadians also fitted some RAM Kangaroos with Wasp II flame-throwing equipment, replacing the hull machine-gun. These 'Badgers', as they were redesignated, were effectively used by the 4th Canadian Armoured Brigade (Lake Superior Regt), during Operation VERITABLE.

The Museum vehicle was rescued from the SPTA ranges near Imber on Salisbury Plain, where it was being used as a hard target for small arms. It was rescued by A Squadron 4th Royal Tank Regiment and restored to exhibition condition by 27 District Workshops, REME, Warminster, in 1984-85, as the plate on its front records.

Gordon Highlanders of the 15th Scottish Division, part of the British Second Army, drive into the village of Tilburg, Holland in October 1944.

SPECIFICATIONS

Manufacturer:	Montreal Locomotive Works.
Conversion	79th Armoured Division, UK (1944)
Pattern Date:	1942
Condition:	non-runner
Engine:	Continental R-975, 9-cylinder radial, petrol-fueled, 400 bhp at 2,400 rpm
Max. Speed:	25 mph
Range:	144 miles
Armour:	1 - 3½"
Armament:	Browning .30-inch machine-gun
Crew:	2
Length:	19'
Height:	6'4"
Width:	9'1"
Weight:	24.5 tons

Australian Cruiser Tank Mk I
(AC1 Sentinel)
8049

After the outbreak of war in 1939, the Australians realised, as did the Canadians, that they could not rely on either Britain or America for their military equipment. Mr A. Chamberlain, an Ordnance Production Engineer, was therefore sent to the United States to study tank production and an expert was sent out from Britain, Colonel W. D. Watson, in 1940 to join the Australian Army Design Directorate. A third tank expert is also worthy of mention, namely a Frenchman named Perrier, who had been working in Japan but had escaped to Australia at the last minute.

The ambitious idea was to produce Cruiser tanks in Australia – which was astonishing because, at the time, they did not even manufacture their own motor cars! In 1940, specifications were issued by the General Staff, for a tank in the 16-20 ton range, with average armour protection of 50mm, a top speed of around 30 mph and armed with a 2 pdr and two machine-guns.

Watson and Chamberlain were impressed by the automotive components of the American M3 medium tank and, during the design of the AC 1, retained many of these features. In May 1941, after many problems in the manufacture of parts and casting of the armour for the vehicle, the AC 1 design was dropped in favour of a new lighter design of tank, around 16-18 tons, designated the AC 2. However, this design was also found to be impractical and by September the AC 1 design was given top priority. The engine layout (devised by Perrier) was quite remarkable with one of the three Cadillacs mounted in between and above the other two in a clover leaf pattern, driving into a central gearbox. It is also possible that he was responsible for the selection of the Hotchkiss suspension.

October 1941 saw the completion of the casting of the first hull, as a single unit, and the ironing out of the problems with the gearbox and transmission, which enabled the first three pilot models to be delivered in January 1942. As planned, the AC 1 could, apart from the Cadillac engines, be entirely manufactured in Australia.

The Australian cruiser tank Sentinel Mk I.

The first production model, out of a production run of only sixty-six due to inherent weaknesses in the design, was delivered in August 1942 – twenty-two months from the publishing of the General Staff Specifications and only eleven months from the 'go ahead' order to the manufacturer. The shortcomings included problems with the bogie wheel tyres, turret drive gear, engine cooling system and poor firepower provided by the 2 pdr (in later models 17 and 25 pdrs were mounted).

On manoeuvres, a Sentinel takes an obstacle at speed.

The sixty-six vehicles that were completed served only in training roles, as, by the time they were delivered, there were sufficient American M3s to equip Australian armoured units.

The Museum's Sentinel was donated by the Royal Armoured Corps in 1949. The serial number T41525 is just a nominal number given to the tank by the Museum staff on its arrival.

SPECIFICATIONS

Manufacturer:	Chullona Tank Assembly Shops, NSW.
Casting:	Bradford Kendall Ltd, Sydney.
Pattern Date:	1942
Condition:	non-runner
Engine:	3 Cadillac V8 41-75, petrol-fueled, water-cooled, 350 bhp
Max. Speed:	30 mph
Range:	200 miles
Armour:	25 mm - 65 mm
Armament:	Co-axially mounted 2 pdr QF and Vickers .303-inch machine-gun, Vickers .303-inch machine-gun hull front
Crew:	5
Length:	20'9"
Height:	8'4½"
Width:	9'1"
Weight:	28 tons

T 34/85 II

Our companies opened fire at about 800 yds but it was ineffective. We moved closer and closer to the enemy… Very soon we were facing each other at 50-100 yds. A fantastic exchange of fire took place without any visible German success. The Russian tanks continued to advance and all armour piercing shells simply bounced off them.

This graphic eyewitness account* of the first meeting between the German Panzers and the Russian T 34, shows the shock the Germans had when their previously invincible Panzers came up against the T 34s heavy and ballistically designed armour.

In 1931, the Soviet Union purchased two Christie T.3 tanks, developed by the maverick American engineering genius J. Walter Christie. After evaluating and testing the Christie vehicles, Russian tank designers returned to the drawing board and produced various light and medium tank designs, resulting in the A 20 in 1938. The A 20, and the earlier BT series, copied Christie's idea of a tank with the ability to move on either tracks or wheels, though not in the form of the early British wheel-cum-tracks (*see* Vickers Wheel-Cum-Track). The 'Christie suspension' was designed so that the track could be removed and the vehicle driven on four large, weight-carrying wheels (on each side). From this, in 1938, the State Tank Design team led by M. I. Koshkin, who opposed the wheel-and-track feature, and his chief assistant A. Morozov, produced a prototype which was then approved by the Supreme War Council. It was given the designation T 32 and was essentially similar to the A 20 – but running solely on tracks. During the summer of 1939 comparative tests were made and though both had good cross-country performance, the T 32 prototype was preferred, having greater armour protection and firepower.

In August 1939, the Military Council having compared the A 20 and T 32, directed the design group towards the production of a less complicated medium tank with improved track suspension. With the development of the V2 500 hp diesel engine, which powered the T 32, and the superb ballistic configuration and armour plating created by N. A. Kucherenko and M. I. Tarshinov (an early version of which can be clearly seen in the shape of the A 20), the stage was set for the creation of what Guderian considered 'the best tank in any army up to 1943' – the T-34.

Design work was completed by December 1939 and, on the 19th December, the High Command were shown the drawings and models of the new T 34. They were immediately accepted and given the go ahead for production – even before the prototype had been finished. The first two prototypes were tested on a 1,800-kilometre trial run, from Kharkov to Moscow and back in March 1940 and, on its successful completion, production was started, the first production vehicle coming off the line at Kharkov in June. This version was known in the West as the T 34/76,

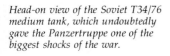

Head-on view of the Soviet T34/76 medium tank, which undoubtedly gave the Panzertruppe one of the biggest shocks of the war.

the '76' referring to the calibre of the 76.2 mm L/30.5 Model 1938 (L 11) main armament. *Side view of the T 34/85.*

General Heinz 'Hothead' Guderian summed up the feelings of the Germans, to the appearance of the menacing and deadly T 34:

> T 34s went into action inflicting heavy losses on the German tanks... I made a report... to the Army Group... I described in plain terms the marked superiority of the T 34 to our Panzer IV and drew the relevant conclusions as they must affect our future tank production... The officers at the front were of the opinion that the T 34 should simply be copied, since this would be the quickest way of putting to rights the most unhappy situation of the German Panzer Troops.

The effect on the morale of both the German armour and infantry was devastating. There were various models of the T 34/76 but by the end of 1943 a completely new version was being manufactured. To provide the Army with more powerful armament the T 34 was 'upgunned', utilizing the turret originally designed for the KV 85 and the new 85 mm tank gun. The result was designated the T 34/85 I.

The T 34 in the Museum is the T 34/85 II, an improved model of the T 34/85 I, introduced in 1947. This was to all intents and purposes the same tank but with improved transmission, armour, fire control and vision devices. They were used extensively in Korea playing an important part in the North Korean's early successes. However, the United Nation's superior tank force eventually overwhelmed them and many T 34s were captured. The Museum's model was captured from the North Korean Peoples' Army by the British Army and then sent to the School of Tank Technology, Chertsey, for evaluation. It was finally donated by them to the Museum in 1952. Unfortunately, precise details of the circumstances of its capture have never come to light, as it was one of many which fell into the hands of the United Nations Forces.

Total production of T 34s of all models until 1945 reached forty thousand and of 34/85s alone some twelve thousand.

*The Russian War Machine 1917-1945 Edited by S. L. Mayer.

SPECIFICATIONS

Manufacturer:	Soviet State Arsenals, U.S.S.R.
Pattern Date:	1947
Condition:	non-runner
Engine:	V-2-34, 12-cylinder, diesel-fueled, water-cooled, 500 bhp at 1000 rpm
Max. Speed:	32 mph (cruising 25 mph).
Range:	280 miles.
Armour	18 mm - 75 mm
Armament:	85mm ZiS S-53 Model 1944 maingun 2 7.62 mm machine-guns
Crew:	5
Length:	26'7"
Height:	8'
Width:	9'10"
Weight:	31.5 tons

Tiger 1 Ausf E (Sd Kfz 181)
Pz Kpfw VI

The first tank to be designated 'PzKpfw VI' was the 'Neubau Fahrzeuge (NbFz)' – new construction vehicle – of 1933-34, however work did not begin on the true 'Tiger' until 1937, when Henschel of Kassel were told to design a close support infantry tank of 30-33 tons, mounting a 7.5cm howitzer, to be known as the Durchbruchswagen (DW1) – the breakthrough tank. Work was however halted the following year and Henschel ordered to switch their design team to a much heavier 65 ton tank project (VK 6501). Two prototypes were built but the project was then stopped and Henschel told to go back to the DW1 project. By 1940, they had produced an improved design, known as DW2, which weighed 32 tons, had a five-wheel torsion bar suspension and mounted a 7.5cm L/24 howitzer. After trials the Army Weapons Branch altered the basic requirements, saying that the gun should be the long barrelled L/48. At the same time they brought three other firms into the project – Porsche, MAN and Daimler-Benz. The new tank was to be known as the VK 3001 and it would have a similar superstructure to the PzKpfw IV, but with a new suspension comprising seven interleaved bogie wheels. The project was however scrapped at prototype stage.

At the same time as ordering work to begin on VK 3001, the Heereswaffenamt had also ordered the design of a 36 ton tank, the VK 3601, the specifications coming from the Fuhrer himself. They included a high velocity gun, thick armour and a top speed of 40km/h (25mph). Henschel built a prototype in March 1942, however, before it appeared work on both the VK 3001 and VK 3601 projects virtually ceased in order to concentrate on another new tank, the VK 4501, which was designed to mount a tank version of the lethal 8.8 cm FlaK 36 gun. Hitler certainly favoured the use of this gun which had already proved itself in ground combat. The order for the new tank was placed in May 1941 and had included a pronouncement that work had to be completed in time for the prototypes to be demonstrated on Hitler's next birthday – 20th April 1942.

In view of the limited time available Henschel decided to incorporate all the best features of their VK 3001 (H) and VK 3601 (H) designs into the new project, to be known as the VK 4501 (H) of which they would produce two models, one with a 7.5 cm gun, the other mounting the 8.8 cm. Porsche did much the same to produce their VK 4501 (P), which was also known as Tiger (P). After much hard work both firms met their deadline and the demonstration took place at Rastenburg on Hitler's birthday. Dr Ferdinand Porsche was a personal friend of the Fuhrer, so it must have been annoying for both of them to discover that the Henschel design H1, was clearly

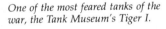

One of the most feared tanks of the war, the Tank Museum's Tiger I.

A rear view showing the height of the flat tail plate, carrying the cylindrical silencers and air pre-cleaners. The Tiger was, supposedly, vulnerable to attack from the rear. In fact, the thickness of the armour at the hull rear is 82mm, thicker than the side plates, which are only 62mm thick.

the best of the contestants, despite the fact that a production order for Tiger (P) was already in full swing at Nibelungwerke in Linze, Austria, with the first delivery scheduled for July 1942. However, as a result of the demonstration and further trials, the H1 design was chosen for production, which was to commence in July/August 1942, the order being for 285 to be built by May 1943. Thus began the production of the PzKpfw VI Tiger Ausf H, which over the next three years would also be called Tiger E, or Tiger I, or Pzkpfw VI Tiger Ausf E.

In an AFV Technical Intelligence Report, issued by MI 10 in February 1941, the PzKpfw V1 was described as a 45 ton tank, with 75mm armour, 75mm main gun with two subsidiary 2cm guns and four machine-guns. It was also supposed to be 36 feet long, 10 feet wide, 6 feet high, with a crew of eighteen and a top speed of 25 mph! In reality, the 57 ton production version was the outstanding design of the war. It featured, apart from the renowned 8.8 cm main gun, armour protection of up to 100 mm and was powered by a 21-litre Maybach V-12 petrol engine – replaced after December 1943 by the HL 230 P45 of 24 litres. It was the first German tank fitted with overlapping road wheel suspension, with triple overlapping and inter-leaved steel disc wheels with solid rubber tyres. This system, combined with the eight independently sprung torsion bar axles on each side ensured the most efficient weight distribution. Major advances were also made in the method of hull and superstructure construction, which were welded throughout. Large plates were used in both hull and turret, to simplify assembly, and the interlocking armour plates had steps cut at the joints which acted as seats for the welds. It could be driven on two types of track one for travelling on roads (21 inches) or wider cross country tracks (28½ inches).

The first units to receive the Tiger I were the 1st SS Panzer Division Leibstandarte *Adolf Hitler* and the 2nd SS Panzer Division *Das Reich*. They first saw action on the Russian Front in 1942, where they were used in limited numbers and on unsuitable terrain, which lessened their impact. The British first encountered the Tiger in Tunisia, in February 1943, but, having advance warning of the attack, engaged the Tigers at close range and destroyed both the Tigers being used in the assault. Production continued for two years, until August 1944, by which time 1,350 had been built. Although an outstanding vehicle, each Tiger took 300,000 man hours to produce and cost 800,000 Reichmarks. In the same time, two Panthers could be built and, for the same cost, three ME 109s could be produced.

THE BOVINGTON TIGER

On 21st April 1943, Churchills of 48 Royal Tank Regiment came into contact with a German armoured force, at Djebel Djaffa, and during the fighting damaged a Tiger. It had already knocked-out two Churchills when it was hit by two rounds from a Churchill's 6 pdr, one hitting the gun mantlet and injuring the commander, the other damaging the turret ring. The crew bailed out, without destroying the tank, leaving A Squadron 48 RTR with the first captured Tiger I, in working order.

Having been examined in situ, it was moved to Tunis where it was seen by HM King George VI and the Prime Minister, Winston Churchill. It arrived in Britain in October and was immediately sent to the School of Tank Technology (STT), Chertsey, for technical evaluation. During November it was put on public display on Horse Guards Parade, before returning to Chertsey for a complete strip down and investigation. Later, in 1944, it was sent to the Gunnery School, West Lulworth, for gunnery trials.

This vehicle No 250112, (turret No 131) of 3 Platoon, 1 Kompanie, Schwere Panzer Abteilung 504, is one of the star attractions of the Museum. A number of visitors to the Museum have reported seeing a ghostly uniformed figure in the Tiger, who was dubbed by the Press 'Herman the German'.

Unfortunately, after the strip examination carried out by the STT, the Tiger was no longer a runner but the Museum workshop staff, with the help of the Friends of the Tank Museum, are determined to return it to running condition. The project gained impetus in 1990, through the backing of PRISM, a special fund run at the Science Museum for the restoration and preservation of scientific material, and the enthusiasm of Stephen Hembry, one of the Friends. A full and detailed restoration programme has been drawn up which will take two to three years to complete, as it involves stripping the vehicle down completely and rebuilding it to full running order. So far (mid-1991), the gearbox has been fully restored, the engine partially restored, the turret removed together with all components from the hull, which has now been steam cleaned prior to shotblasting.

SPECIFICATIONS

Manufacturer:	Henschel & Sohn, Kassel
Pattern Date:	1943
Condition:	non-runner
Engine:	Maybach HL 210 P45, petrol-fueled, water-cooled, 600 bhp at 3,000 rpm
Max. Speed:	38 km/ph
Range:	140 km
Armour:	25 - 100 mm
Armament:	8.8 cm KwK 36 L/56, 2 7.92 mm MG 34.
Crew:	5
Length:	8.45 m
Height:	2.93 m
Width:	3.70 m
Weight:	57 tons

TOG II*

In September 1939, the General Staff outlined details for a new Super Heavy Tank to be known as the A 20. The specifications issued were;

a. to be resistant against enemy 37mm and 47mm anti-tank ammunition, and 105mm gun-howitzer ammunition at 100 yards range.

b. have a maximum speed of 9 mph and cross heavily shelled country at a speed of 5 mph.

c. be able to cross a 16-foot trench, and a 7-foot vertical obstacle.

d. have a crew of eight – commander, driver, front gunner, four sponson gunners, wireless operator.

e. armament was to be; one field gun in the front hull, two 2 pdrs and 7.92mm Besas co-axially mounted in side sponsons, two 7.92mm Besas – one to fire to the rear and one to the front, four 2-inch smoke mortars to give all round fire.

Shortly after the A20 project began, Sir Albert Stern, who played such an important part in tank design and development at the beginning of World War One, gathered around him some of the other technical experts who had worked with him in early days and persuaded the Cabinet to form these individuals into the Special Vehicle Development Committee (SVDC). The SVDC, was made up of such venerable names from the tank pioneering days as W. G. Wilson, Sir William Tritton, Harry Ricardo, Sir Ernest Swinton, Sir Eustace Tennyson D'Eyncourt and others. It soon came to be nicknamed 'The Old Gang', hence the name of the tank, TOG.

Work began in February 1940 and in May an order was placed for a second tank. They became known as TOG I and TOG II respectively. TOG I was a throwback to the early days, not only reminiscent in looks to the rhomboidal vehicles of the World War One, but also having old-style track plates and side sponsons. The first trial in September 1940, on the prototype, showed the vehicle (even without real armour) weighed in at around 73 tons! Trials continued and as late as spring 1944, TOG IA, as the modified version had been redesignated, was undergoing minor alterations. After this time, having been moved to Chobham on a huge 100 ton transporter, little was ever heard of it again.

TOG II, ordered in May 1940, was similar in design and layout to TOG 1, apart from the top run of the tracks which was lowered, possibly to allow for a larger

The 80-ton monster named after 'The Old Gang', TOG II.*

turret ring – thus allowing for larger armament. It was planned not only to have side sponsons and a 3-inch howitzer in the hull front, but a turret armed with a triple gun-mounting, consisting of a 3-inch howitzer, with a 2 pdr anti-tank gun mounted on its right and a Besa on the left. After trials in 1941, new tracks were ordered, the turret was changed, and various other modifications were made, all on the drawing board.

In September 1941, TOG II was redesignated as TOG II*, as so many modifications had either been made, or were planned. Eventually, in the prototype TOG II*, which can be seen in the Museum, the hull gun and side sponsons were dropped, improvements were made to the final drive and suspension and the turret was redesigned to mount a 17 pdr anti-tank gun, which was later seen on the Challenger A 30. Trials continued until May 1943 when, although now weighing 80 tons, it performed flawlessly in front of the members of 'The Old Gang'. However, as the War Office showed no interest, plans for further versions – TOG IIR and TOG III were already being planned – and so work on TOG II* ground to a halt. Shortly afterwards, TOG I was broken up and TOG II* was presented to the Museum.

Interestingly, it had been the mobility and firepower of Hitler's Panzers during the *Blitzkrieg* in France which had shown the Allies the proper and effective employment of armour. This lesson spelt out the death-knell of the ponderous TOG, because it showed that World War Two would not be fought in the static way of the Great War – conditions for which TOG had been designed. Yet, although never seriously considered by the War Office for production, its development continued up to, and after, the time when the Germans began developing their heavy tanks *e.g.* the Tiger series and Maus, the 180 ton colossus.

For many years TOG II* stood outside the Museum rusting and forlorn, being used as a waste basket for drink cans, cigarette packets and other litter. Then, in 1990, with the completion of the Tamiya Hall, it was at long last brought under shelter so that restoration work could at last begin. This is now well in hand.

SPECIFICATIONS

Manufacturer:	William Foster and Co. Ltd., Lincoln
Pattern Date:	1940
Condition:	non-runner
Engine:	Paxman Ricardo, 12-cylinder, 600 hp diesel, driving two electric generators which drove two electric motors
Max. Speed:	8.5 mph
Range:	50 miles (approx)
Armour:	12 - 64 mm
Armament:	17 pdr and 2 7.92 mm Besa machine-guns
Crew:	8
Length:	33'3"
Height:	10'
Width:	10'3"
Weight:	80 tons

Black Prince A 43

In December 1943, Allied tanks were still outarmoured and outgunned by the Germans. Neither the Challenger A30 nor the Sherman Firefly, both mounting 17 pdr guns, had adequate armour to engage the German Panther and Tiger tanks on equal terms. It was, therefore, planned to put the 17 pdr gun into the more heavily armoured Churchill. The design of the turret was to be governed by the size of the 17 pounder gun, although consideration was to be given to the chance of later 'upgunning' to an even larger calibre gun such as the 3.7-inch Mark V1, the penetration performance of which was 25 per cent better than that of the 17 pdr.

Owing to the larger turret ring diameter required for the 17 pdr gun, the standard Churchill hull was too narrow. An enlarged version was therefore designed, using as many Churchill A22F components as possible, with the same armour thickness.

Vauxhall built six pilot models (designated A43 and known as Black Prince) and full production could have started by the spring of 1945. Unfortunately, the combination of two other factors caused the project to be shelved. First, the standard 350 bhp Bedford engine was not powerful enough for the A43, which weighed 49 tons (8 tons heavier than Churchill). Secondly, by the time plans had been made to replace it with the 600 hp Rolls-Royce Meteor engine, a decision had been taken to concentrate the future tank programme on one class of tank only, namely, the 'Universal', which was on the point of being built. Only one of the six pilot models, still exists, 'No 4 Pilot' which has been with the Tank Museum since being donated by the Royal Armoured Corps in 1949.

The A43 'Black Prince' also known as the 'Super Churchill' was basically a Churchill VII, with a wider turret which mounted a 17pdr gun.

SPECIFICATIONS

Manufacturer:	Vauxhall Motors Ltd, Luton, Bedfordshire.
Pattern date:	1944
Condition:	non-runner
Engine:	Bedford Flat-12, petrol-fuelled, 350 bhp
Max. Speed:	10.6 mph
Range:	100 miles
Armour:	25 - 152 mm
Armament:	Quick Firing (QF) 17 pdr Mk 6; 2 x BESA Mk 2 machine-guns, 1 bomb thrower 2-inch
Crew:	5
Length:	28' 11"
Height:	9' 0"
Width:	11' 3"
Weight:	49 tons

A front view of the same vehicle.

Engesa EE 9 Mk V
(Cascavel – Rattlesnake)

The EE9 Cascavel was designed to meet Brazilian Army requirements by ENGESA (Engesa Engheneiheiros Especialiazados), in July 1970. In November, following completion of the prototype and trials, a pre-production order was placed for ten CRR (Carro de Reconhecimento Sobre Rodas) vehicles.

The CRR was to be a 6 x 6 wheeled armoured car, designed for the traditional roles of reconnaissance, direct and indirect fire support and flank guard for tank units. The first production vehicles, delivered in 1974, were slightly longer and wider than the prototypes, had a different wheelbase and were fitted with a turret armed with ex-US M3 37mm light tank guns. These first production models, built for export, were fitted with the French H 90 turret [see Panhard AML 90]. Current production vehicles are fitted with an Engesa ET90 turret armed with an Engesa EC90 gun. It has many common components with the E11 Urutu APC, also built by Engesa, and many of the automotive parts are of standard commercial type, thus easily available.

The vehicle in the Museum is a Mark V donated by Snr Nelson Ribeiro, head of Engesa Engheneiheiros Especialiazados of Brazil, at a handover ceremony on 26th June 1986 (see plate on front of AFV). It is powered by a Mercedes-Benz six-cylinder diesel engine. Its cross country performance is helped by a central tyre inflation system, which allows the driver to adjust the tyre pressures to suit the terrain. It has an all-welded hull of dual hardness armour, consisting of a thin inner skin and an outer layer of hardened steel. It also has increased protection on the frontal arc and is specially designed for urban warfare, to give maximum protection against booby traps, petrol bombs and grenades. It was valued at £45m in 1984.

By 1984, 2,550 Cascavels had been produced and they have seen action with both the Brazilian Army and Marines, the Iraqi Army during the war with Iran and during the invasion of Chad by Libyan-backed guerrillas in 1983.

The Museum's Cascavel on Battle Day, being crewed by the Society of Friends of the Tank Museum.

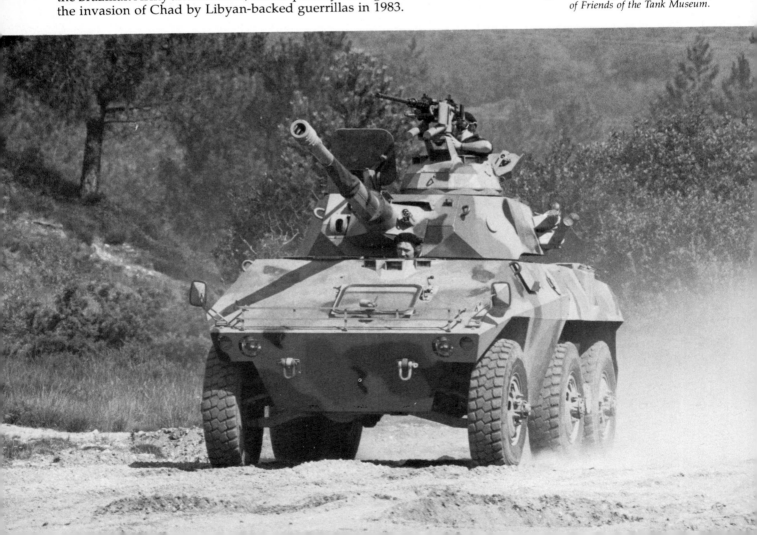

SPECIFICATIONS

Manufacturer:	Engesa Engheneiheiros Especialiazados, St Paulo, Brazil.
Pattern Date:	1978
Condition:	runner
Engine:	Mercedes-Benz OM 352 A, 6-cylinder, turbo-charged, diesel-fuelled, 190 bhp at 2800 rpm
Max. Speed:	100 km/ph
Range:	880 km
Armour:	8.5 - 16mm
Armament:	90mm EC-90
	2 7.62mm machine-gun
Crew:	3
Length:	6.2m
Height:	2.6m
Width:	2.64m
Weight:	13.5 tons

A Cascavel on trial in the desert.

Centurion Mk 3
02 ZR 18

On 23rd February 1944, final specifications for the A 41, first formulated by the Army Council in September 1943 (maximum width 10 feet 6 inch, armour protection against the German '88', weight limit of 40 tons and armed with a 17 pdr) were completed and the Tank Board recommended that twenty prototypes should be built.

In May 1944, it was decided that of these twenty, five were to mount one 17 pdr, plus one 20mm Polsten, one 7.92mm Besa in the rear of the turret (the rear-firing machine-gun was abandoned in June, due to problems with stowage); five would mount one 17 pdr, one 20mm Polsten with optional linkage and be fitted with a rear escape door; five would mount one 17 pdr, one 7.92mm Besa with optional linkage and be fitted with a rear escape door; and the final five would mount one 77mm main gun, one 7.92mm Besa with optional linkage and rear escape door.

The first A41 prototype was delivered for trials by the Royal Ordnance Factory (ROF) Woolwich Arsenal in April 1945. By this time, it had acquired the name Centurion, originally allocated to the A 30 (which had eventually been named Challenger). It weighed 45½ tons and had a maximum speed of 23.7mph. Prior to the end of the trial, it was suggested that a number of prototypes should be trialled under active service conditions before the end of hostilities in Europe, under the codename Operation SENTRY. Six prototypes, three from ROF Nottingham and three from ROF Woolwich, were handed over at FVPE in early May 1945, to a detachment of the Guards Armoured Division, who were then attached to the 22nd Armoured Brigade in NW Europe for trials, but not before VE Day.

During June and July, gunnery trials were held and although the main gun performed well, there was criticism of the 20mm Polsten (it took up too much space in the turret) and although the 7.92mm Besa was satisfactory, users preferred the more reliable Browning. However, the opportunity was taken to show the vehicle

The present curator's Centurion Mk III is seen here in its layback position on the 'Hook' feature in Korea, May 1953. Note the additional .50 Browning mounted on top of the turret and the Canadian searchlight for ad hoc night illumination.

A Centurion from 1st Royal Tank Regiment presses on during Winter Warfare Training on the Soltau NATO ranges in Northern Germany.

to other units and the general comments were more favourable. Reliability, ease of maintenance, performance and fighting characteristics were all most satisfactory and many considered it to be the best medium tank they had ever seen. The 'sharp end' users also appreciated the chance to express their opinion and recommendations on the prototypes.

As none of the criticisms were really of any major significance, production of 800 Centurions was authorised; 100 A41* Centurion Mk Is mounting a 17 pdr with linked 7.92mm Besa; the remainder were to be A41A Centurion Mk IIs, of which the first hundred would mount the 17 pdr and the rest, the 20 pdr. Centurion Mk IIs incorporated a number of improvements, including a cast turret, commander's vision cupola, combined gunner's periscope sight and co-axial machine-gun.

A total of 4,423 Centurions of different models were produced, the majority of which were 2,833 Mk IIIs. The major improvements in the Mk III were in the engine, which was the more efficient 650 bhp Rolls-Royce Meteor Mk 4B (Marks I and 2 had 640 bhp Meteor Mk 4A), the Ordnance Quick Firing 20 pdr main gun and its Gun Control Equipment. Many other modifications and refinements were constantly being made during production. As with the Mark II, all ammunition was stowed beneath the level of the turret ring – research having proved that this increased the tank's chances of survival. During the war, the destruction of many tanks had been due to ammunition fires.

The Mark III production began in ROF Barnbow and Vickers Armstrong in 1948. It was the first British vehicle that could fire accurately on the move, thanks to the gyroscopic equipment designed by Metropolitan-Vickers Co. The first regiment to be equipped with the new tank was the 1st Royal Tank Regiment stationed in Detmold, Germany. In 1948, the vehicle numbers were changed from Roman to Arabic numerals – the Mk III becoming Mk 3.

The Centurion Mk 3 first saw action in Korea, with 8th Hussars, 5th Inniskilling Dragoon Guards and 1 RTR, where the general opinion was that it was the best tank of the war, far superior to the T 34/85. The accuracy of the 20 pdr gun allowed targets to be engaged at ranges of up to 3,000 yards. Centurions also saw action with 6 RTR at Port Said (Mark 5s) during the Anglo-French intervention to occupy the Suez Canal, in 1956, and with 16th/5th Lancers in the Wadi Misrah (Mark 10s) during the Aden Emergency in the early 1960s.

Centurions were also exported to a wide range of overseas customers, including

Australia – the first overseas purchaser, with whom they saw action in the paddy fields of Vietnam in the sixties. Canada, Denmark, Egypt – though after the Suez crisis the Egyptian Army was re-equipped by Soviet designed tanks; the Centurions were retained until they were lost to the Israelis, during the Six-Day War (coincidentally, during the October War of '73, the Egyptians captured some Israeli Centurions. Holland, India, Iraq, Israel – at one time the Israeli Army had around 1,000 Centurions in service. First procured in 1959, the Israeli Centurions initially fought against Panzer IVs of the Syrian Army, frequently destroying them at ranges of 4,000 metres. In 1967, they began work to improve its performance and reliability and replaced the engine with the US Teledyne Continental AVDS-1790-2A, used in the M48A2 Patton. With the introduction of the Israeli home-produced tank the Merkava, the firm Soltam proposed to rearm the obsolete Centurions with a self-contained 155mm SPG turret, incorporating the Tampella 155mm Calibre 39 howitzer. Jordan, Kuwait, New Zealand, South Africa, Sweden and Switzerland also bought significant numbers of Centurions.

The Museum's cut-in-half Centurion was originally a Mark 2, one of the first 400 made; it was then converted to a Mark 3 and ended its service life as a Mark 5. It was then kept at the Vehicle Depot, Ludgershall, where it deteriorated badly and was destined to become a target on the Gunnery School ranges at Lulworth. However, the present curator 'rescued' it and persuaded the Director of ROF Leeds to cut it in half. It was restored to Mark 3 standard and sectionalised at Royal Ordnance Factory Barnbow as part of an apprentice training programme.

The other Mark 3 in the Tank Museum, located in Korean corner, is badged up for the Troop Leader's tank of 2 Troop, C Squadron, 1 RTR, which the present curator commanded during the 'Hook' battle of May 1953.

SPECIFICATIONS

Manufacturer:	Royal Ordnance Factory Barnbow, Leeds. Vickers Armstrong Ltd, Elswick.
Pattern Date:	1946
Condition:	non-runner
Engine:	Rolls-Royce Meteor 1VB, V-12, water-cooled, petrol-fueled
Max. Speed:	21.5 mph
Range:	32.5 miles cross country, 62.5 miles on roads.
Armour:	17 - 152 mm
Armament:	Ordnance Quick Firing 20 pdr Mk 1 Co-axial 7.92 mm Besa machine-gun
Crew:	4
Length:	28'3"
Height:	9'7
Width:	11'11"
Weight:	50 tons

Chieftain 900
53 MS 09

In 1981, as a private venture, the Royal Ordnance Factory, Leeds, began the design and development of a main battle tank, to be known as 'Chieftain 900'.

Chieftain 900 was to be based on the late production Chieftain chassis, modified to accept the CV 12 powerpack, which comprised a Rolls-Royce Condor 900E twelve-cylinder engine and the Self Changing Gears Ltd TN12-1000 transmission. Both the hull and turret were designed with low silhouettes and featured the British-developed Chobham armour, the combination providing exceptionally high protection against all battlefield anti-tank weapons. Special attention was also given to improve hull protection against anti-tank mines. For firepower, the 120mm L11A5 rifled tank gun was used, fitted with a fume extractor, thermal sleeve, laser sight and muzzle reference system (MRS – for easier sighting and gun alignment). A fire control system was not fitted, so that any prospective client could choose from a number of different systems – according to their specific operational requirements.

Two prototypes were completed by April 1982, No 53 MS 09 and No 53 MS 10. The vehicle in the Museum is prototype 53 MS 09, which was originally a Chieftain Mk 5/3P manufactured in the late 1970s, the version used by the Iranian Army. In 1980, it was exhibited at the British Army Equipment Exhibition (BAEE) as 'Chieftain 800', re-engined with the 800 hp version of the Rolls-Royce Condor CV 12. In 1981, after the launch of the Chobham-armoured 'Chieftain 900', this vehicle was then converted to simulate the 900 configuration, with tin work instead of extra armour.

Front on to the impressively shaped Chieftain 900.

The other prototype, 53 MS 10, had a 900 hp engine but, again, not genuine Chobham armour.

Side view of the same vehicle. Extra add-on armour has since been fixed to Chieftain 900 (cf: Gulf modified Challengers).

They were both exhibited at BAEE in 1982, but as there were no orders, the project was abandoned four years later. Both vehicles were then sent to the School of Electrical and Mechanical Engineering (SEME), Bordon, Hampshire, to reduce the number of Challengers diverted for training, but, after standing outdoors for some time, 53 MS 09 was sent, on permanent loan, to the Tank Museum in 1988.

In 1990, Vickers Defence Systems requested the loan of this AFV for experimental purposes in connection with the development of Challenger 2 and other AFVs. The Tank Museum was happy to oblige. It is now back in the collection.

SPECIFICATIONS

Manufacturer:	Royal Ordnance Factory, Leeds.
Pattern Date:	1977
Condition:	runner (1990)
Engine:	Rolls-Royce Condor CV 12 turbo-charged, diesel-fuelled, 800 bhp at 2,300 rpm
Max. Speed:	52 km/ph
Range:	400-500 km
Armour:	Chobham armour
Armament:	L11A3 120mm gun. Co-axial 7.62 mm machine-gun. Anti-aircraft 7.62 mm machine-gun
Crew:	4
Length:	10.8 m
Height:	2.44 m
Width:	3.51 m
Weight:	55 tons

Conqueror Mk 1
40 BA 86

Shortly after work began on the design and development of Centurion, the Government's newly-formed Department of Tank Design put forward plans for two other classes of vehicle: a light tank, FV300; and a 'Universal' tank, FV200. The 'Universal' tank was to be designed so that it could be easily adapted to carry out a variety of other roles – flame-thrower, mineflail, bridgelayer, AVRE, APC and SP Gun.

By 1949, it was realised that the cost of developing the full range of the FV200 series, some twenty-two variants, would be too high and work ceased on FV201 (A45 Universal Tank with 20 pdr gun). This was partly due to the versatility of the Centurion and the discovery of its potential to fulfil a wide variety of roles, as it could provide the basis for any necessary variants (ARVs, Bridgelayers etc). However, with the appearance of the Russian JS-3 (Joseph Stalin) heavy tank, with its powerful 122mm gun and 160mm thick armour, the need for FV214 Heavy Gun Tank (120mm main gun) was established.

FV 214 'Conqueror', developed from the original FV201, was powered by the Rolls-Royce Meteor M120 V-12 petrol engine (developing 750 bhp in the FV201 but modified to produce 810 bhp, at 2,800 rpm, in Conqueror), with Merritt-Brown transmission and modified Horstman suspension. Its main armament, mounted in a well-shaped turret, was derived from an American 120mm tank gun, which in turn was derived from an anti-aircraft gun. It was the first British tank in which the shell case and projectile were separate, however, a large brass shell case was used to hold the propellant rather than a bag charge, and this made it very heavy and cumbersome to load, while the stowage was only possible for 35 rounds, mounted in a well-shaped turret.

By 1952 the first pilot model was running and by 1955 twenty were going through troop trials in BAOR. In all, 180 vehicles were produced and Conqueror spent its service life as a potential Tank Destroyer

A detailed view of a Prototype Conqueror.

Throughout its career Conqueror was plagued by electrical and mechanical malfunctions and, although necessary (to combat the threat of the Soviet heavy tanks), it proved difficult and generally unpopular with the crews.

A Conqueror heavily disguised as a Christmas tree.

SPECIFICATIONS

Manufacturer:	Royal Ordnance Factory, Dalmuir.
Pattern Date:	1955
Condition:	runner
Engine:	Rolls Royce M120 V-12, water-cooled, petrol-injection. 500 bhp at 1,000 rpm
Max. Speed:	20 mph
Range:	95 miles
Armour:	1" - 3"
Armament:	120mm L1A1 main gun. 1 x .30-inch Browning machine-gun coax and one in Comd's cupola.
Crew:	4
Length:	38'0"
Height:	11'
Width:	13'1"
Weight:	65 tons

Leopard 1

The re-establishment of the Army of the Federal Republic of Germany in 1955, ten years after its disarmament at the end of the war, led to the decision to equip its combat units with AFVs, weapons and equipment from outside sources. The American M 47 and M 48 tanks were bought in, allowing training of crews to commence, but it was decided that a new tank would have to be designed, partly so that their armament industry could be rebuilt, and also because it would allow German industry access to the lucrative worldwide arms market.

The new tank was to be designed in conjunction with the French and Italians, and common specifications for the 'Europanzer' were agreed, known as 'NATO Finabel 3A5', and published in 1956. On 25th July 1957, the Technical Department of the German Ministry of Defence proposed the following further specifications;

A combat weight of 30 tons; a maximum height of 7 feet 3 inches; a radius of action of not less than 220 miles; a gun capable of defeating 150 mm of armour (5.9 feet) at an angle of 30 degrees and an effective range of 2,500 metres (2,374 yards); an air-cooled multi-fuel engine.

The three powers agreed that mobility and firepower was more important than armour protection, as modern anti-tank weapons could defeat the defensive properties of modern armour.

Two German design consortia were set up: Team A, led by Porsche, which included Atlas-MaK, Luther-Werke and Jung-Lokomotivfabrik; and Team B, led by Ruhrstahl, which included Henschel and Rheinstahl Hanomag. The French concentrated their design and construction effort with Atelier de Construction d'Issy-les-Moulineaux, the designers of the AMX-13.

Both German teams finished their designs and produced wooden mock-ups in 1959; at the same time the French team had finished their prototype, designated AMX 30. By January 1961, the A Team, led by Porsche, had produced two prototypes, designated A1 and A2, and in September, Ruhrstahl's Team B completed its two prototypes, designated B1 and B2. All four prototypes used the same turret, de-

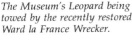

The Museum's Leopard being towed by the recently restored Ward la France Wrecker.

veloped by Rheinmetal, armed with a 90mm Rheinmettal gun and all were powered by the Daimler-Benz 838 engine.

The Museum's Leopard fitted with the new Royal Ordnance 105 IWS gun.

After comparative trials at the Bundeswehr Proving Ground, Trier, the A1 and A2 prototypes proved the better – the torsion bar suspension was preferred, they were less expensive, easier to produce and closer to the traditional German tank concept. Team A received an order to produce twenty-six of the A-2 models, now known as the Porsche Standardpanzer. Team B also had an order placed for six B-2 type vehicles, but by Autumn 1962, further development on the B-2 project was discontinued. By January 1961, the 90mm gun had been replaced by a 105 mm Rheinmetal main-gun, and further trials were being held on another alternative – the British L7A1 105 mm (later developed into the L7A3), for which the Germans later opted.

From these trials, and the trials of the French vehicle at Bourges, differences of view became apparent between the three nations. Ultimately, this led to the French deciding to continue building their own tank, the AMX 30, and, later, the Italians also opted out of the Europanzer project. The Germans decided to carry on regardless and trials of the prototypes were completed in May 1962.

The Standardpanzers being produced incorporated many changes from the A-2 prototype, including a ten-cylinder 830 hp engine, and a redesigned turret to fit the Vickers L7A3 tank gun (one of the most advanced in the world, designed for the Centurion and also used on the US M60). From March to September 1962 trials continued, and many minor improvements and modifications made. In October, the Standardpanzer was redesignated Leopard.

Comparative trials between the Leopard and the AMX 30 in September 1963 proved that although the Leopard had a greater combat weight (40 tons compared with 36 ton for the AMX 30), it had better cross country performance, could move 10 per cent faster on roads and had 18 per cent better acceleration. The French gun could only fire one type of projectile, whereas the British L7 could fire APDS, HEAT and HESH.

In 1963, during the summer, the German Ministry of Defence awarded Krauss-Maffei of Munich, the management contract of the 2,700 firms involved with the project. In the following years, Leopards were lent or exchanged with a number of countries, for trials, and at the end of the day the Leopard emerged with flying colours, resulting in sales to Australia, Belgium, Canada, Denmark, Greece, Italy, Netherlands, Norway and Turkey.

The Museum's Leopard 1, a pre-production prototype, model J 03, was one of two swapped for two Chieftains, by the Army, for trials at MVEE. It was recently used in a trial by Royal Ordnance, on their Improved Weapon System (IWS) – gun, projectile and charge system. The IWS 105mm gun can be easily fitted to older generation battle tanks, giving them up to date performance. Basically, it is a high pressure development of the well proven L7 gun, used by most Western 105mm gunned tanks, and offers performance similar to 120mm smoothbore weapons. It has a chromium plated barrel, uses the latest developments in gun steels and fires a new high performance APFSDS round, in addition to existing NATO 105mm ammunition.

SPECIFICATIONS

Manufacturer:	Jung-Jungenthal Lokomotivfabrik, Kirchen-Sieg, Federal Republic of Germany
Pattern Date:	1962-63
Condition:	non-runner
Engine:	Daimler-Benz MTU MB 838, 10-cylinder, multi-fuel engine, 818 bhp
Max. Speed:	62.5 km/h
Range:	550 km
Armour:	25 - 70mm
Armament:	L7A2 105mm gun, (but currently mounting the IWS gun)
Crew	4
Length	9.543m
Height:	2.613m
Width:	3.25m
Weight:	39.5 tons

M 48 Patton
9A5213

By October 1950, deficiencies were very apparent in the M 47 (an amalgamation of the 46 ton M46 hull and the turret of the 36 ton T42), so a design study began at the Detroit Arsenal to produce a tank with lower ground pressure, greater range, improved armour protection and distribution, a more efficient fire control system and improved ammunition for the 90mm main gun. The overall mobility and manoeuvrability of the M47 were also to be retained.

On 8th December 1950, the US Army approved the Detroit Arsenal's design study and an order for the design and manufacture of the 'Tank, 90mm gun, T48' was placed with the Chrysler Corporation. Chrysler began work on 22nd December 1950 and by 14th December 1951, the first T48 prototype was completed at the new Chrysler factory, Newark, Delaware. It was first shown to the Press and public on 1st July 1952, and was later named 'Patton M48' by Mrs Beatrice Ayer Patton, wife of the brilliant, but flamboyant, American tank commander, General George Patton killed in 1945 in a road accident.

When compared to the M47, the T48 showed many improvements, improved armour protection, improved fire control system, a quick change gun-barrel for the T 139 gun (developed by the Watervliet Arsenal), wider tracks and improved suspension. It was also the first American tank to have a one-piece cast hull, the turret was also cast, which not only was simpler to produce but better ballistically. The new design also allowed for a larger turret-ring size (85 inches) which meant that a larger gun could be installed at a later date. However, the engine and transmission were the same as the M47, which was known to have a very high fuel consumption and therefore a short battle range of only 85 miles, so with greater weight and less fuel the range of the M48 was reduced to only 70 miles (with a reduced maximum speed).

In the Spring of 1955, the Americans held Exercise DESERT ROCK VI in the Nevada desert. A 35-40 kiloton atomic weapon was detonated at the Atomic Energy Commisions test site on 3rd May, at 5.10 am. Task Force Razor, consisting of fifty-five

An M48 in Vietnam.

Compare the extra protection on the turret of this US Cavalry M48A3 with the last photograph – great for semi-static operations, but they would never all stay on if the tank had to move in a hurry!

M48s with support, were in hull down position only 3,000 yards from ground zero and not only survived the blast but motored through the fallout zone to arrive at their target by 6.00 am. Three unmanned M 48s were placed, at different angles, only 500 yards from ground zero and though damaged, they remained intact and could be driven away. The tank facing head on to the blast was blown backwards 10 feet but was only superficially damaged. The worst damage was done to the vehicle at a three-quarters angle to the blast, which was rolled over, stripping the tracks – though it was extensively damaged, the tank's engine was still sound. The three tanks eventually survived six nuclear explosions and two of the vehicles, though not combat worthy, were still able to drive away.

The M48 saw action in Vietnam (almost all were the M48A3 model), the first unit to deploy them being the 3rd Marine Tank Battalion, which disembarked at Da Nang. It was three years before tank met tank. Seventy per cent of tank losses were due to mines, and, to begin with, their task was mostly jungle-busting (creating routes through the jungle), bunker busting and as mobile pillboxes. During the Tet offensive in 1969, there were several tank to tank engagements (mostly against North Vietnamese PT 76s) all of which ended in clear victory for the M48. Later, in 1972 there were a series of engagements between Vietnamese Republican tanks and Vietcong T 54s and PT 76s – the M 48 made short work of them, destroying some of the enemy tanks at a range of up to 3,200 yards.

The Museum's M48 is a potential runner and was a gift from the US Army in July 1969.

SPECIFICATIONS

Manufacturer:	Chrysler Corporation, Newark, Delaware.
Pattern Date:	1952
Condition:	potential runner
Engine:	Continental AVI-1790-8, 12-cylinder, 825 bhp
Max. Speed:	30 mph
Range:	290-310 miles
Armour:	51 mm - 110 mm
Armament:	90 mm M41 main gun
	7.62mm M73 co-axial machine-gun
	.50-inch M2HB machine-gun in cupola.
Crew:	4
Length:	28'6"
Height:	10'3"
Width:	11'11"
Weight:	46.5 tons

Panhard AML 90 (H90 turret)
EA 33524

In 1956, following the successful use of the British Ferret scout car by the French in North Africa, the French Army issued specifications for a similar vehicle but with more powerful armament. Panhard, who were already working on a heavy armoured car, received the contract to build the new prototype, which was completed in 1959. After trials with other prototypes, from Saviem and DEFA-AMX, the Panhard Model 245 was accepted by the French Army as the Automitrailleuse Légère. The first production models were delivered in 1961.

The 4 x 4 AML 90 has an all-welded hull with a Hispano-Suiza H 90 turret, mounting a 90mm D 921 F1 main gun. The 4HD petrol engine develops 90 bhp and it has two gearboxes in one, the low-range box for cross country use and the high-range box for normal road use. The independent suspension consists of coil springs and hydro-pneumatic shock absorbers, and the tyres are fitted with unpuncturable Hutchinson inner tubes.

By 1986, some four thousand five hundred AML 4 x 4s had been built, in some thirteen variants, and they have seen service with thirty-five or more countries. The model in the Museum, described above, is no longer under production. It was captured during the Falklands War at Port Stanley, where it had remained throughout the conflict. It was never used in action as it could not cope with the boggy conditions prevalent in the battle areas. It was brought back from the Falklands by the Blues & Royals and went immediately to RARDE Chertsey, who gave it to the Museum in June 1983. Unfortunately the clutch was damaged during trials and has not yet been replaced, so the vehicle is a non-runner.

The AML 90 in French Army service disembarking from a landing craft.

SPECIFICATIONS

Manufacturer:	Panhard et Levassor
Pattern Date:	1978
Condition:	non-runner
Engine:	Panhard 4 HD, 4-cylinder, petrol fueled, air-cooled
	90 bhp at 4700 rpm
Max. Speed:	90 km/h
Range:	600 km
Armour:	8 - 12mm
Armament:	D 921 F1 90mm main gun
	7.62mm machine-gun
Crew:	3
Length:	5.11m
Height:	2.07m
Width:	1.97m
Weight:	5 tons

A side view of the vehicle.

Scorpion
00 SP 97

In the early 1960s, the United Kingdom still had many defence commitments around the world, so, as the political situation at home led to demands for cuts in spending on defence, the need for highly mobile, air-portable troops and equipment had been recognised. A study was therefore made by the Royal Armoured Corps on the feasibility of air-portable armoured vehicles, as replacements for the ageing Saladin and Saracen wheeled vehicles, to equip these mobile strategic forces.

From the Light Weight High Mobility Tracked Vehicles concept came the call for a series of vehicles to be known as AVRs (Armoured Vehicle Reconnaissance), including a Fire Support version (replacing Saladin), an anti-tank vehicle, a specialist anti-APC (Armoured Personnel Carrier), a Liaison vehicle (replacing Ferret), an APC, a Command vehicle and a Stretcher carrier. Later, the designation was changed to Combat Vehicle Reconnaissance (Tracked), CVR (T), family of vehicles. There was also to be a family of CVR (W), wheeled vehicles, which resulted in Fox and Vixen.

The vehicles were to have commonality of automotive components, the same engine layout and they were to be built on a common chassis. The hull and turret were to be built out of a newly-developed aluminium-zinc-magnesium alloy, known as E74S (AA 7039 type) – ballistically superior to the US lightweight aluminium-manganese alloy armour used on the M113. For performance, the militarised version of the proven Jaguar XK J60, 4.2 litre six-cylinder, OHV engine, was chosen.

In September 1967, Alvis Ltd of Coventry won the contract to design the vehicle and in 1970, after extensive trials of the prototypes (first completed in January 1969), they were given the go-ahead for production. The family comprised; CVR (T) Fire Support – Scorpion; CVR (T) Anti-APC – Scimitar; CVR (T) APC – Spartan; CVR (T) ARV – Samson; CVR (T) Anti-Tank – Striker; CVR (T) ACV – Sultan; and CVR (T) Ambulance – Samaritan.

In early 1973, the Blues and Royals, stationed at Windsor, were the first British regiment to be issued with Scorpion, followed later in the year by the 17th/21st Lancers, at Wolfenbuttel, West Germany. It took some time for the full potential of the vehicle to be realised but generally it was accepted with enthusiasm and excitement. Every chance was taken to show Scorpion to the Press – the track exerts less ground pressure than a walking man, and to prove it, the vehicle drives over a ballpoint pen, on grass, leaving it intact (this trick has been, mistakenly, performed

A camouflaged Scorpion of 16th/15th The Queen's Royal Lancers, on reconnaissance patrol during the Turkish invasion of Cyprus, July 1977.

Scorpion in winter dress; having such low ground pressure (51 lb ft/sq in), Scorpion has proved itself able to cope with all terrains and conditions.

on concrete with rather less impressive results!). Scorpion also performed a lap around the famous West German Grand Prix racing circuit – the Nurburgring.

In 1982, during the Falklands War, four Scorpions and four Scimitars of the Blues and Royals took part in the recapture of the Falklands. All came back intact despite air attacks by A4 Skyhawks and one of the Scorpions driving over an anti-tank mine – the tank was damaged but the crew were unhurt, apart from ringing ears and headaches. Having landed at San Carlos they were needed as back-up for 5th Brigade at Bluff Cove. Headquarters estimated that it would take up to thirty-six hours to make their way back tracking from San Carlos, along proven routes. However, the Blues and Royals were confident of their vehicles ability to cope with the most rugged terrain and took a supposedly impassable southern route, reaching their objective in only six hours. The Brigade Commander commented;

> We badly needed the armour back-up of the Blues and Royals but, although I had ordered them to join me, I never expected they would be able to make it in the time they did. When I saw them winding down the mountain towards us, it was one of those moments I am not likely to forget.

CVR (T) was therefore proven combat capable in the most arduous conditions, and the MoD commented;

> Of particular note was the excellent cross country mobility and high reliability of Scorpion and Scimitar, emphasising the value of tracked vehicles in such terrain conditions.

This was reinforced by the lack of success of the Argentine wheeled Panhard armoured cars, in the peat bogs and heavy going of the Falklands.

Various models of the CVR (T) series again proved their worth during the Gulf War.

SPECIFICATIONS

Manufacturer:	Alvis British Leyland Ltd, Coventry.
Pattern Date:	1971
Condition:	non-runner
Engine:	Jaguar XK, 6-cylinder, water-cooled, petrol-fueled, 195 bhp at 5,000 rpm
Max. Speed:	50 mph
Range:	400 miles
Armour:	Aluminium-zinc-magnesium alloy (*see* above 'Armour')
Armament:	L2A31 76 mm maingun. 7.62 mm co-axial machine-gun
Crew:	3
Length:	15'8.5"
Height:	6'10¾"
Width:	7'4"
Weight:	7.8 tons

T-54

The T-54 was developed from the T-44, designed in 1944 and produced, in small numbers, from 1945 until 1949. The main improvements of the T-44 over the T 34/85 were its torsion bar suspension, well-shaped hull and its turret – similar to the T 34/85 turret but bigger and better shaped.

However, the T-44 proved unreliable in service and design work began on an improved version on the T-44 hull, with a new, more thickly armoured turret, designed to mount the D-10 100mm gun. After completion of the prototype, in 1946, and successful state trials, the vehicle was designated the T-54. Production began in 1949 and in 1951 the turret was redesigned to improve the ballistic shape. The V-12 water-cooled diesel engine (type V 54) was mounted transversely at the rear of the hull, as was the transmission. Torsion bar suspension was used.

By 1951, the T-54 had replaced the T-34/85 and T-44 on the assembly lines and had become the standard medium tank of the Soviet Ground Forces. The definitive version, with further turret improvements (deletion of the rear turret overhang – so that the turret appeared almost hemispherical), which proved to be the final configuration of the series, was first seen in 1953. Between 1946 and 1958 it is believed that around thirty-five thousand T-54 tanks were produced and production continued after this time in Czechoslovakia (total production by 1985 was approximately two thousand five hundred), Poland (total production approximately three thousand) and China – who manufactured the T-54 as the Type 59, later modified as the Type 69 – (total production approximately sixteen thousand by 1985). Other armies equipped with the T-54 include Egypt, India, Romania, East Germany and Israel.

Two Polish T54As in winter camouflage. Note the 12.7mm DShK AA MG mounted in front of the loader's hatch.

This good rear view of T54As on parade shows the excellent ballistic shape of the turret. The turret handrails are for infantry to grasp, whilst the brackets on the rear are for smoke canisters.

The Israeli army captured many T-54s and T-55s during the 1967 and 1973 conflicts, modifying them for their own use – replacing the 100mm gun with a 105mm and the engine with a General Motors 8V-71T engine, developing 890 bhp.

In the 1970s, the Museum was approached by the Israeli Defence Forces for an exchange of vehicles. The Israelis wanted a Cromwell tank, one of the first tanks used by them, two having been hi-jacked from a British depot in 1948. The exchange was for a Syrian T-54 captured in battle and then modified for service with the Israeli Defence Forces. Note the extra machine-gun mountings on the turret, the trackguard extensions and rubber headlights, all Israeli modifications. Unfortunately, the Israelis would give no further details of the tank's history as the story of its capture was still classified. It arrived at Bovington Camp in August 1976 with a seized engine and was restored to running order at 18 Base Workshop. It came to the Museum in May 1977, but has never been a satisfactory runner. However, between 1989 and 1991, the engine and transmission has been overhauled by Perkins Engines of Shrewsbury and it is hoped to have it running again by 1992.

SPECIFICATIONS

Manufacturer:	Soviet State Arsenals, U.S.S.R.
Pattern Date:	1946
Condition:	potential runner
Engine:	Type V54, V-12, water-cooled, diesel-fuelled, 520 bhp
Max. Speed:	48 km/ph
Range:	400 km
	600 km (long range tanks).
Armour:	20 - 203 mm
Armament:	D-10T 100mm main gun.
	3 7.62mm machine-guns
Crew:	4
Length:	9 m
Height:	2.4 m
Width:	3.27 m
Weight:	35.5 tons

Vixen
03 SP 85

In step with the development of Scorpion and the other members of the Combat Vehicle Reconnaissance (Tracked) series, there was also a great deal of work done to find a successor to replace the ubiquitous Ferret Scout Car, because it was felt that there would always be a continuing need for a wheeled recce vehicle. This led to the development of the Combat Vehicle Reconnaissance (Wheeled) family, of which the Fox was the prime vehicle, being in effect, a fast, lightweight armoured car, mounting the highly effective 30mm cannon (*cf:* Scimitar). Fox entered service in 1973. The next member of the CVR(W) family was to have been the Liaison version, CVR(W)L, appropriately named as 'Vixen', the mate to Fox. Work on the prototype of Vixen, FV722, was begun in the late sixties and a handful of prototypes produced by the ROF in their factory at Barnbow, Leeds. However, Vixen was not to survive, being cancelled in the defence cuts of December 1974.

Vixen had been designed for use by all arms, to carry men and a wide variety of equipment about on the battle area, with the same speed and protection as the Fox. Automotively it is identical to Fox, having the same engine, transmission, power-pack, suspension and power steering. Because it has the same overall size and weight as Fox, it shares such common mobility features as swimming and air portability. To save weight, Vixen was constructed of aluminium alloy armour, which, as well as giving protection against heavy and medium machine-guns and shell splinters, contributed to performance and allowed more equipment to be carried, as well as crew and passengers. CVR(W)L could easily accommodate a driver, a commander and up to two passengers.

The small turret is mounted on a 30-inch (.75 metre) Roballo ring and the commander has five periscopes for all-round vision, plus a periscope sight, linked to a 7.92mm GPMG controlled and fired by him. A periscope is provided for each

Vixen on trials at the test grounds in Chobham.

Side view of the same vehicle.

passenger, while the driver has a counterbalanced 'up and over' hatch giving excellent forward vision when open, and fitted with a wide angle day periscope (which could be replaced for a passive infra red night driving periscope). A flotation screen was provided, propulsion in the water and steering being by the road wheels.

The Vixen on show is one of only two remaining and first came to the Museum in June 1982 as a gift from MVEE. At that time it was a non-runner, being deficient of a steering unit and exhaust. It was restored to running condition 18 Base Workshop, REME in 1982-83.

SPECIFICATIONS

Manufacturer:	Royal Ordnance
Pattern Date:	1971
Condition:	runner
Engine:	4.2 litre Jaguar Type J60 No 1 Mk 100A
Max. Speed:	65 mph
Range:	320 miles
Armour:	aluminium alloy
Armament:	7.62mm machine-gun
Crew:	2 + 2 passengers
Length:	13'8"
Height:	6'7"
Width:	7'
Weight:	6.25 tons

Type 69-II Main Battle Tank

The Type 69 MBT was first seen in public during a parade at Zhangiakou, outside Bejing (Peking) in the People's Republic of China, in September 1982. Some sources claim that production of the Type 69 started in 1969, however, most say that volume production did not begin until the early 1980s. The Type 69 was a development of the Type 59, which was itself developed from the Soviet T 54 MBT as supplied to China in some quantity in the early 1950s, the Type 69 differs from the Type 59 mainly in the areas of armament, fire control and night vision equipment.

First production models, Type 69-I, were fitted with a 100mm smoothbore gun, however, extensive trials later proved that a rifled 100mm was more accurate, so all Type 69-IIs are fitted with the rifled gun. It fires Chinese developed HEAT, HE, APHE & APFSDS ammunition, with at least three types of fin-stabilised (APFSDS) rounds having been produced including one with a semi-combustible case. The main armament is stabilised in both elevation and azimuth, the tank is also fitted with TSFCS (Tank Simplified Fire Control System) and side skirts. The laser rangefinder is fitted externally and so is vulnerable to shell splinters and small arms fire, however, there is the option of TSFCS-L where the laser rangefinder is combined with the gunsight in a single, internally mounted unit.

Other versions of the Type 69 include the 37mm SPAAG, first seen in 1988, twin 57mm SPAAG, Type 84 AVLB and Type 653 ARV.

Iraq initially placed orders for some 100 to 200 Type 69s and the first deliveries were made, via Saudi Arabia in 1983. Over a three year period up to late 1987, a total of between 1800 and 2000 were estimated to have been delivered.

The Museum's exhibit was one of a number of Type 69s captured by units of the British 1st Armoured Division during Operation 'Desert Sabre' and shipped home in the late Spring of 1991 to Marchwood, near Southampton. It was first shown to the public on Sunday, 28th July 1991, when the GULF WAR exhibition was opened

The Type 69, with a T 62 behind it, seen on the road at the side of the Museum. It was captured during the Gulf War and shipped back to the UK.

Good view of the Museum's other Type 69 on the coach park after being unloaded. Like its partner it was in service with Iraqi armoured troops.

by Brig Patrick Cordingley, DSO, who commanded 7th Armoured Brigade in the Gulf. It has been left exactly as it was when captured, apart from some superficial damage caused in transit. In due course, however, we hope to put the AFV back into running order.

SPECIFICATIONS

Manufacturer:	Chinese State Arsenals
Pattern Date:	1981
Condition:	non-runner
Engine:	Type 12150L, V-12 diesel
Max. Speed:	50 km (31 mph)
Range:	420-440 kms
Armour:	20mm to 203mm
Armament:	1 x 100 mm, 2 x 7.62 mm machine-guns (one coax, one hull) and 1 x 12.7mm machine-gun
Crew:	4
Length:	8.657 m
Height:	2.807 m (to axis of AA MG)
Width:	3.298 m
Weight:	37,000kg (36.42 tons)

Museum Accession Numbers